SCIENCE AND ETHICAL VALUES

The John Calvin McNair Lectures
of the
University of North Carolina at Chapel Hill

The John Calvin McNair Lectures

FRANCIS H. SMITH, *God Manifest in the Material Universe*
FRANCIS LANDEY PATTON, *Authority and Religion*
DAVID STARR JORDAN, *The Stability of Truth*
HENRY VAN DYKE, *The Poetry of Nature*
ARTHUR TWINING HADLEY, *Some Influences in Modern Philosophic Thought*
FRANCIS G. PEABODY, *Christian Life in the Modern World*
GEORGE EDGAR VINCENT, *The Social Vision*
JOHN DEWEY, *Philosophy and Politics*
FREDERICK J. E. WOODBRIDGE, *The Purpose of History*
HUGH BLACK, *The Great Questions of Life*
EDWIN GRANT CONKLIN, *The Direction of Human Evolution*
PAUL SHOREY, *Plato's Relation to the Religious Problem*
CHARLES ALLEN DINSMORE, *Religious Certitude in an Age of Science*
ROSCOE POUND, *Law and Morals*
WILLIAM LOUIS POTEAT, *Can a Man Be a Christian Today?*
CHARLES REYNOLDS BROWN, *A Working Faith*
THORNTON WHALING, *Science and Religion Today*
HARRIS E. KIRK, *Stars, Atoms, and God*
ROBERT ANDREWS MILLIKIN, *Time, Matter, and Values*
GEORGE F. THOMAS, *Spirit and Its Freedom*
ARTHUR H. COMPTON, *The Human Meaning of Science*
WILLIAM ERNEST HOCKING, *Science and the Idea of God*
KIRTLEY F. MATHER, *Crusade for Life*
EDMUND W. SINNOTT, *Cell and Psyche*
C. A. COULSON, *Science and Christian Belief*
BENTLEY GLASS, *Science and Ethical Values*

SCIENCE AND ETHICAL VALUES

by BENTLEY GLASS

THE UNIVERSITY OF NORTH CAROLINA PRESS · CHAPEL HILL

501
G54a

Copyright © 1965 by
The University of North Carolina Press
Manufactured in the United States of America
Library of Congress Catalog Card Number 65–25599
Printed by Kingsport Press, Inc., Kingsport, Tennessee

PREFACE

The three essays gathered here represent a natural extension of ideas expressed in a more preliminary form in the first and last of the three essays contained in an earlier book, *Science and Liberal Education,* which like the present volume was stimulated by an endowed series of lectures at one of our great American universities. I am deeply indebted to the University of North Carolina for the opportunity to pursue my thoughts about the relations of science to social and moral ideas more fully, in the form of these John Calvin McNair Lectures.

In the first of these three lectures I have picked up the thread of thought developed in my earlier essay on "Darwinian Evolution and Human Values." Without too much repetition, I hope, I have tried here to show that ethical values do grow out of the biological nature of man and his evolution. These values are relative. The values at one level of biological organization, such as that of the gene or cell, may stand in conflict with the values at the level of the individual, just as the values at the level of the individual may conflict, and often do, with those that inhere at the level of the human population or living community of species. Reso-

APR 15 '66

lution of these conflicts of ethical values is one of the gravest human problems. Sin follows the knowledge of good and evil. Innocence is largely compounded of ignorance of consequences. As man's knowledge of consequences grows he is ineluctably faced with problems of choice between the values of lower levels of living organization and those of higher levels, between the values for today and those for tomorrow, between the values for the local group and those for the wider, all-encompassing community of life.

The essay "Human Heredity and the Ethics of Tomorrow" treats more fully the ethical problems and quandaries earlier introduced in the essay entitled "Genetics in the Service of Man." Here I have endeavored to illustrate more specifically, within the field of my own scientific specialty, the nature of the stupendous ethical problems that will face mankind in the very near future, as man begins to apply his knowledge to the control of his own reproduction and future evolution.

Finally, I have reversed the line of thought and have tried to demonstrate that science itself is a subjective, social, human enterprise completely dependent upon its own ethical foundations. In these days when the natural sciences are assuming so great a role in the development and alteration of our civilization, when every man must modify his ways of life decade by decade to accommodate himself to the changes wrought by scientific technology in human culture, far too little thought is given to the ethical basis of our science. To be sure, I am not the first to write about this subject, and perhaps I have added very little to what has been said by others. Nevertheless, I find that on our university and college campuses the cleavage between our "two cultures" exists not so much because scientists are little interested in the arts or because humanists are little conversant with the great scientific concepts of the twentieth century, as because the scientist is too blithely confident that more and more scientific knowledge will be good for man irrespective of its applications and too hopefully confident that others can cope with the ethical problems he creates, while the humanist fears the aggrandizement of science in our society and fails to appreciate the nature of the ethical problems that science generates, or perhaps even to recognize their existence.

A sound philosophy of human life must bring these streams of thought together, to interact fruitfully and compassionately. Today, the philosophy of science means mostly the structure of science and its logic; the history of science is a scholarly pursuit little related to the study of social change. Both the philosophy and the history of science are needed as a part of the incorporation of science into our humanistic tradition and learning. Yet they are not enough. Even the study of the sociological relations of science, today in so rudimentary a state of infancy, will not be enough. Besides these, we need a fuller, more frequent consideration of the relations of science to ethics, to the full range of human values. To the future development of such a humanistic study this small book is dedicated.

BENTLEY GLASS

Johns Hopkins University
June 16, 1965

CONTENTS

1

THE EVOLUTION OF VALUES

[A Natural History of Value]

To examine the problem of values—their origin, their permanence, their absoluteness or relativity—from the point of view of a biologist may yield insight, even though treatment of human values strictly from a biological, evolutionary viewpoint cannot promise any final resolution of the problem. A natural history of values may be possible, in spite of the fact that values cannot be measured in strictly quantitative terms nor defined and treated in strictly scientific fashion. Charles Darwin, in the *Descent of Man*, opened up a consideration of this subject; and John Dewey in an early essay on "Evolution and Ethics" did so too.[1] Many persons—scientists, sociologists, philosophers, and others —have reached diametrically opposed views on the matter. Let us not prejudge it, whether we lean toward Thomas Henry Huxley's outcry against the cruelty of nature and the blindness of natural selection, or prefer the roseate belief of Julian Huxley in indefinite cosmic progress toward higher levels of social co-operativeness and idealism. Some may hold with Darwin's own belief that the differences between man and other animals are but matters of degree, capable of explanation by natural selection. Others may agree with David Lack, a noted modern student of evolution, who holds that "an essential part of human experience and human nature lies outside the terms of reference of science." [2] Can both be right?

It would be hard to find any biologist today who questions that natural selection is the principal agent of evolutionary change. Doubts about this assailed many thinkers in the first three decades of the twentieth century because of a seeming inconsistency, or even conflict, between ideas of evolution by means of genetic mutations, on the one hand, or by natural

1. John Dewey. 1898. Evolution and ethics. *The Monist*, 8: 321–41.
2. David Lack. *Evolutionary Theory and Christian Belief: The Unresolved Conflict* (London: Methuen, 1957), pp. 105–6.

selection, on the other. These doubts have been resolved through fuller knowledge gained from experimental studies of mutation and selection. Both processes are in fact essential, but mutation provides only the raw material, the grist for the mill of evolution. Without hereditary variations, as Darwin clearly recognized, natural selection would have nothing transmissible to work upon, nothing permanent to shape into the adaptations of living organisms. The mutations of the genes and chromosomes supply those hereditary variations, in a way Darwin did not suspect. Nevertheless, there is no impulse toward improvement that is in any way inherent in the mutations themselves. By far the great majority of them, perhaps as great a proportion as 99 per cent of all new genetic changes, are detrimental. They are fated to be eliminated from the population, quickly in some cases, more slowly in others, but inevitably in all.

Today it is more clearly seen why this must be so. Each gene controls some particular step in the chemical machinery of the cell. It does this by preserving and transmitting the special chemical information needed for the synthesis of a particular protein, most often one of the enzymes that govern some particular reaction such as a transformation of some particular substance into another. When a gene mutates, the enzyme under its control either cannot be made at all, or else is made in some abnormal configuration that either lacks activity altogether or is partially impaired. The chemical step is then wholly or partly blocked. Now if, in the eons of time during which organic evolution has proceeded, inadequate and unnecessary chemical processes have been eliminated through natural selection and have been replaced by more efficient and better-controlled processes, there should be very little superfluous chemistry in the make-up of the vital machinery of life. This is indeed what the biochemist finds, whether he examines the metabolism of a bacterium or a yeast cell, a green plant or a man. Superfluous chemistry has been eliminated; the steps which remain are all vital and necessary to the well-being of the organism. That is, we do not possess, to any significant degree, useless enzymes and unnecessary chemistry. It follows that almost any conceivable alteration of the genes that control the enzymes, that regulate the chemistry, will be highly unfortunate in effect. Indeed our analyses show that a large proportion of them—one quarter or more—are so drastic in effect that they would be lethal were it not for "nature's wisdom" in generally providing us with two genes of every sort, so that incapacitation of one of them is not fatal so long as the other is able to keep the chemical machinery in operation. It is therefore very significant that mutation is a rather random, undirected kind of natural event. Of two exactly similar genes in the nucleus of a cell, the mutation of one is practically never accompanied by mutation of the other.

The undirected character of mutation also relates to the fitness of the organism within its environment. If we suppose a completely static and uniform environment, natural selection should long ago have produced perfect adaptation, and evolution would then have ceased. In that case, no doubt, man would never have appeared on the earth, which would have been successfully and permanently pre-empted by some lowly but perfectly adjusted, non-evolving worm or maybe amoeba. In actuality, however, our terrestrial habitat contains many different kinds of environments, occupied and unoccupied, and the conditions of existence vary continuously with the cycle of day and night, the pageant of the seasons, and the greater cycles of geologic change. Earth, water, and air provide innumerable varieties of conditions; and adaptation involves ceaseless adjustment and readjustment to the alteration of conditions. Yet since mutations are not inherently directed toward better fitness, we cannot expect that the right mutation will arise at precisely the right time. Instead, the mutation process is constantly infusing the populations of each species with every possible sort of mutation, the great majority of them being, as I have said, detrimental or even lethal. Yet one or more of these, in some particular combination, may produce a genotype that is better adapted to the new conditions of life imposed by the changing environment. In that case, natural selection will tend not only to eliminate the detrimental mutations from the collective genes of the entire population—from its gene pool, as we say—but will also tend to preserve and increase in number those genes that confer an adaptive advantage.

Natural selection remains, then, the essential directive force in evolution, just as Darwin conceived it to be. Nevertheless, our ideas of what processes are involved in selection have been reshaped very considerably because of experiments on selection conducted in the past three decades. Darwin emphasized the "struggle for existence," that often fierce competition for survival between members of the same species which results in death without reproduction. The differential survival of hereditary types in a population signifies the death of the less well-adapted and the less fortunate. It implies disease, hunger, and suffering—the cruelty of nature. It aroused Thomas Henry Huxley's passionate protest against any tie between ethics and evolution. It has no less evoked the emphasis by others upon the evolutionary origin of mutual aid and co-operation, of social bonds and, eventually, of love. Yet this is only half of what natural selection involves. In quantitative terms of the frequencies of competing genes in successive generations, very often a gain in frequency by one gene and a loss by another depends not so much on the survival to maturity of their possessors as it does upon the possessors' relative fertility—the abundance of their offspring—after they arrive at maturity. In a harsh environment, differential selection may play the lead. Many genotypes are eliminated in embryonic or fetal stages, many others in the period before reproductive maturity is attained. But in an abundant environment, when the food supply is ample and new and previously unoccupied environments open up, the survival rate of all offspring may be high; and then differential fertility becomes the leading type of natural selection. Far too little attention has been given to the importance of such differences until recently.

Obviously, the two kinds of selection as a rule work hand in hand. In a situation where thousands of seedlings or hundreds of tadpoles perish for every one that survives to maturity, the parent generation must be very fertile or the species will soon disappear. Conversely, whenever on account of parental care a high proportion of the young that are conceived are able to become adult, demands on the fertility of the parents are greatly reduced. And in general, this less wasteful pattern of reproduction has proved more successful in the struggle between species for coexistence. Nevertheless, the differences in fertility of different genetic types become even more important within these less fertile species than they are in the more fertile species having a higher mortality of the young.

Adaptation grows out of the progressive changes in the composition of the gene pool of a population or species as the mutations that occur are exposed to natural selection. Those genes and genotypes are perpetuated which under existing conditions enable their possessors to survive to reproduce, and to reproduce more abundantly. Biological fitness is simply this, however it may jar our moral sensibilities—it is compounded of high viability and high fertility, and nothing besides. If evolution then contains anything that bears on the nature of values, it must lie here. For in evolutionary terms the value of any characteristic, of any structure or physiological capacity, of any mode of behavior or form of action, may be measured quite simply, by the following criterion: does it contribute to the survival of the genetic strain, population, and species? If it does so—if it promotes either the survival or the fertility of the individual—the trait is adaptive. It has evolutionary *value*.

Consider briefly the problem of pain. Most people think of pain as inherently evil, a part of the cruelty of nature. The biologist sees it in quite a different light. Pain is a sense that leads effectively, in most instances, to the avoidance of injury. Occasional individuals have been reported in the medical literature who completely lacked a sense of pain. Their experience was a most unhappy one, since they failed to learn in infancy and childhood to avoid burns, bumps, cuts, and other kinds of injuries. So far as we can tell, plants and invertebrate animals have no sense of pain. A wasp that has had its abdomen completely amputated, a fatal loss, will continue to suck up sugar water as if nothing had happened. Fish seem to have very little if any sense of pain, and it is doubtful whether frogs or snakes experience pain, although certainly, like lower animals, they manifest fear and alarm. Without trying to draw too sharp a line, it may be said that pain seems to be almost exclusively a sense experienced by birds and mammals, that is, by the warm-blooded animals. It clearly possesses evolutionary value, since it reinforces the behavior that leads to avoidance of injury. Among those animals which depend almost exclusively upon instinctive behavior and which possess little or no capacity to learn, the experience of pain would lack teaching value, and in them it seems poorly developed, if present at all. The value of pain, then, is connected with avoidance of injury and is of evolutionary origin. It is a product of natural selection. It is a mark of the capacity to learn from experience and a sign of the sensitivity of the organism's adaptation to its environment.

REPRODUCTION AND DEATH

If living organisms lived forever, there would long since have been no room on the globe for any new ones. Without the existence of new individuals upon which to act, natural selection would not come into play, and evolution would never have occurred. Living organisms arise from one or from two parents of their own species. Populations increase until they run out of space or means of subsistence. There is consequently competition, struggle, death. New individuals replace those that have been born earlier. Hereditary variation produces new types of individuals, some of which prove in time to have superior viability or fertility, and therefore replace their forerunners. In short, reproduction is essential to the evolutionary process.

Thus through reproduction, and especially sexual reproduction, new genotypes arise. If the conditions of the environment are changing, some of the new genotypes may be superior to the older, previously selected ones. They may survive in greater numbers under the new conditions, or they may be more fertile. If the environment is undergoing a progressive, long-term change, the species may step by step undergo a progressive adaptation to the altered environment, through recombination of mutants and selection of superior genotypes. But always this process assumes that the older, less-adapted types are eliminated, that they no longer clutter up the living space, using the food and encumbering the ground. Death is in fact necessary to biological progress, and accidental death, starvation, or slaughter are unlikely to suffice. If the species can through selection build into its own living machinery a basis of obsolescence—or let us call it senescence—there will be better assurance that the older, once adapted but now less well-adapted genotypes will not be in the way of the newer, better-adapted ones. Is this in fact possible? The universal existence among sexually reproducing plants and animals of a life span characteristic of each species shows that it is. Not only death, but senescence and the limited life span, have strong evolutionary value. Oh death, where is thy sting? [3]

THE BIOLOGIST LOOKS AT VALUES

To the evolutionary biologist, values are always relative. There is no absolute fitness, beyond the ability to survive and

3. The relation of natural selection to the characteristic life span of each species has been discussed by not a few biologists, beginning with August Weismann's essays on "The Duration of Life" (pp. 1–66) and "Life and Death" (pp. 111–61), reprinted in *Weismann on Heredity,* ed. E. B. Poulton, S. Schönland, and A. E. Shipley, 2nd ed. (London: Oxford University Press, 1891). Most recently, P. B. Medawar has advanced new causes for the evolution of natural death and senescence by means of natural selection, in *The Uniqueness of the Individual* (New York: Basic Books, 1957), pp. 17–70. Yet so far as I know, no one has pointed out the importance for evolution of the replacement of old, existing genotypes by new and different ones, as I suggest here. The basic assumption underlying this postulate is that populations are most frequently stabilized in number. Ever-expanding populations could of course introduce an abundance of new genotypes, even if the older individuals were immortal except for accidental deaths. In general, however, natural selection does exist, populations are in fact under pressure, and habitats and ecological niches are indeed well filled. If the reasoning is correct, population pressure is itself a cause (through natural selection) of the existence of natural death and the limited life span, for those populations and those species will prove superior which replace their genotypes regularly enough to meet the vicissitudes of their environments most effectively.

reproduce in some niche of the earth's enormous variety of habitats. The lethal gene that *always* kills, in every possible terrestrial environment, would be absolutely bad for its possessor. But is there really ever such a gene? When their effects are analyzed biochemically, we find that lethal genes in general kill their possessors because a particular biochemical step is completely or partially blocked, through lack of the enzymatic activity normally controlled by the gene. That means that some product of the reaction is missing, and often that some substrate of the reaction is not used up. Frequently the lethal effect of the mutation may be fully countered if the missing product is supplied, or in some cases if the accumulating substrate is removed.

At the level of physiological processes and morphological structures it is particularly easy to see that adaptive values are always relative. I have often used the example of flies, which in a city such as Baltimore find it to their advantage to have wings and to use them. Only flying flies are likely to get from one garbage pail to another and to find food and mates. But on the island of Kerguelen, lying in the southern Indian Ocean and in the latitudes of the roaring forties, no fly with wings could survive very long. Although the island is a fairly large one, of 1,318 square miles, it lacks trees because of the stormy winds. The grasses and Kerguelen cabbage harbor many species of insects, including flies; but all of the insects, including the flies, are wingless. Mutations that produce winglessness occur in all populations of flies, including those of Baltimore, but only in an environment like that of Kerguelen does such a mutation change from being nonadaptive to become adaptive. On Kerguelen, winglessness has value.

In evolution the values are thus always relative, precisely because they are adaptive. That is, they always involve some relation between the needs of the organism and the external conditions which impose and satisfy those needs. As many who have discussed the problem of values have said, from Santayana and Dewey to the neurologists Coghill and Herrick, this relativity seems to apply to all systems of values. Values always relate intrinsic needs to extrinsic satisfactions. The verb "ought" necessarily involves relations between a system and its surroundings. Does it not follow that a good adjustment or adaptation possesses positive value? In evolutionary terms, most certainly. The deeper question remains: are there other values outside of evolutionary fitness, other values less relative, perhaps? I think that we can hope to approach that deeper question only by carrying our analysis of evolutionary values to the utmost limit, in order to see just how much evolutionary values may indeed encompass.

In the evolutionary progression from simpler forms to the most complex, life has passed through a hierarchy of levels of organization. Among the organisms of today we can readily discern all of these same levels of organization. From the molecular level we pass to the cellular level. Cells are grouped into differentiated tissues and organs. The organs make up the body of a complex individual, such as a human being, but the levels of organized life do not stop here. Individuals collectively form a population belonging to a single species. All the populations coexistent in a single area form a community. The communities of the earth are interknit to constitute a great biome. The values of which we are speaking therefore exist not simply at the level of the individual person. As one progresses from the level of molecules toward the organized community and above it the biome, new values are constantly emerging and older ones undergo a species of change. There is a hierarchy of values that corresponds to the levels of organization which characterize living systems.

STAGES IN THE EVOLUTION OF VALUES

The Molecular Level

At the molecular level our attention is engaged in particular by the enzymes which so marvelously control all living chemistry, and by the genetic materials, deoxyribonucleic acid (DNA) and ribonucleic acid (RNA), which respectively transmit the hereditary information of each species from generation to generation, and convey it to the protein-synthesizing centers of the cell where the enzymes are made. A comparative study of enzymes reveals that, whenever there is an option of different forms of the same enzyme, each capable of mediating the same reaction but with different efficiencies under different conditions, then natural selection tends to establish those forms of the enzyme with greater efficiency, with greater stability, and with optima that in general correspond to the most commonly prevailing conditions of the environment. Other forms of the enzyme, with less efficiency, less stability, or optima at degrees of temperature or hydrogen ion concentrations that do not correspond to ordinary conditions, become replaced by the superior forms.

This kind of selection will of course not proceed in a simple solution in a test tube. It is a part of the total competition between living beings that possess enzymes having different characteristics. Rightly seen, it is at the basis of all natural selection, which must operate upon hereditary variations that modify the chemical controls of life. Genes control the nature and production of enzymes, so the selection of superior genes implies the selection of superior enzymes. Thus, many of the detrimental mutations that have been found to occur can be shown to result not in an entire absence of a specific enzyme but rather in temperature-sensitive enzymes, or enzymes with

THE HUNT LIBRARY
CARNEGIE INSTITUTE OF TECHNOLOGY

antigenic properties similar to the original ones but with greatly reduced activity, or enzymes that seem more readily to combine with some inhibitor such as metal ions that may be present in the cell. Mutants such as these are often said to be "leaky" because they allow a very slight activity of the chemical reaction in question to proceed, or because by some alteration of the conditions they can be made to exhibit a minor degree of activity.

Also at the molecular level are the properties of the DNA and RNA. The DNA, in nearly all living organisms the fundamental hereditary material, alone possesses the capacity to replicate itself. Each strand of the double helix that comprises a molecule of DNA has a backbone of phosphate groups alternating with 5-carbon sugar (deoxyribose) groups (Fig. 1). An organic base, a purine or pyrimidine, is attached to each sugar. As a rule, there are four sorts of these bases in each DNA molecule: adenine, guanine, thymine, and cytosine (Fig. 2). The two strands are linked by weak bonds that form between adenine and thymine and between guanine and cytosine. Thus each strand is complementary to the other, in the nature and sequence of its bases. Inasmuch as the backbone of the DNA molecule is the same from one end to the other, the differentiation of parts of the molecule into different genes must be spelled out by the sequence of the four kinds of bases. There is now a fair amount of evidence to indicate that the code of genetic information consists of three-letter words, if we use the four initials of the bases, A, G, T, and C, as our only letters.

Experiments have been performed which indicate that the DNA replicates itself in a simple but ingenious way. The two strands of the duplex molecule untwist, and each single strand then picks up from the cytoplasm of the cell complementary units, known as nucleotides, each consisting of a

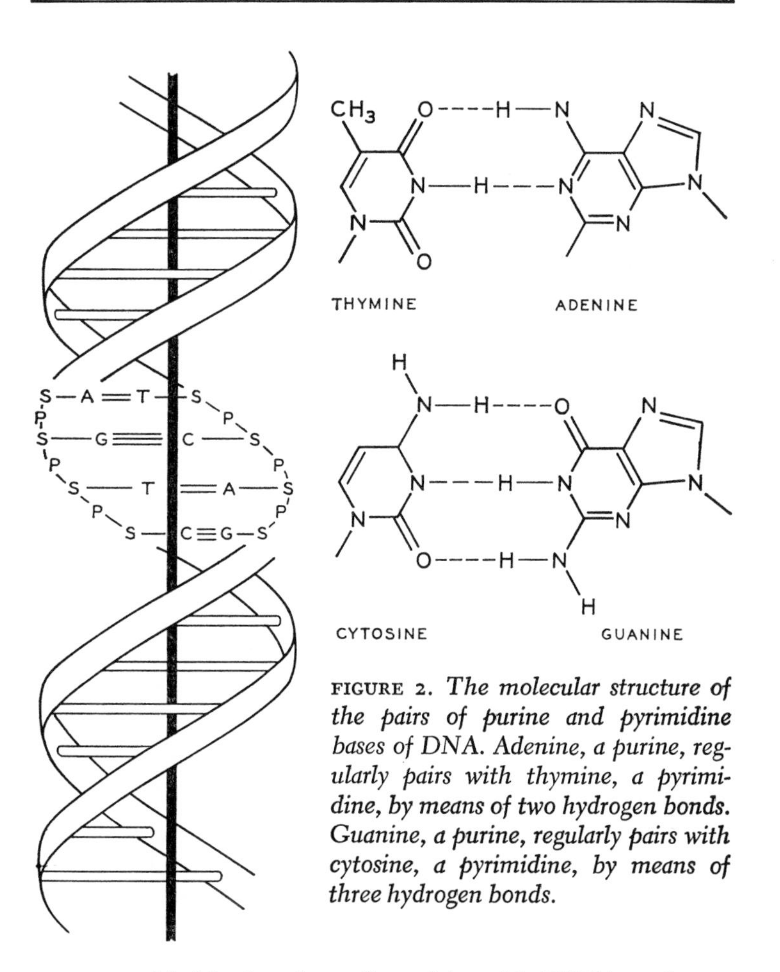

FIGURE 2. *The molecular structure of the pairs of purine and pyrimidine bases of DNA. Adenine, a purine, regularly pairs with thymine, a pyrimidine, by means of two hydrogen bonds. Guanine, a purine, regularly pairs with cytosine, a pyrimidine, by means of three hydrogen bonds.*

FIGURE 1. *Model of a deoxyribonucleic acid (DNA) molecule. In one portion of the double helix the symbols for the repeating sugar (S) and phosphate (P) groups that constitute the backbone of each strand are shown. The paired bases are A, adenine; T, thymine; G, guanine; and C, cytosine.*

base, sugar, and phosphate group. Thus a strand carrying the sequence --C-A-T-- in its array of bases will select from the cell nucleotides with G, T, and A, in that sequence. These then become united into a new complementary strand. Meanwhile the other strand of the original double helix, the one bearing the sequence --G-T-A-- to start with, will have selected nucleotides bearing the bases C, A, and T, in that sequence, and will have bound them by chemical linkages into a complementary strand. Thus the original double helix has become two identical double helices. Each of these will be separated when the chromosome containing them splits and the daughter chromosomes move into different daughter cells.

There are in nature a considerable number of other purines and pyrimidines besides those four that make up most DNA. One of the familiar purines, for example, is the drug caffeine which is abundant in tea, coffee, and certain other beverages. Yet almost without exception, these other bases will not serve as components of DNA; or if by accident they do get into its make-up at some point, they do not participate in the replication process properly, since they fail to attract specific complementary bases to the right sites. The result, from the standpoint of the gene, is a disaster—a detrimental mutation, a loss of specific hereditary information at some point of the genetic material.

The DNA transfers its information to RNA molecules by means of a process analogous to that of replication. Some of the RNA molecules comprise the messenger-RNA that leaves the nucleus of the cell and impresses its directives on the protein-synthesizing units of the cell, the ribosomes (Fig. 3). The RNA possesses a different base instead of thymine, and it has a slightly modified kind of sugar group in each nucleotide, a ribose instead of deoxyribose sugar. These chemical differences appear to be sufficient to confer upon

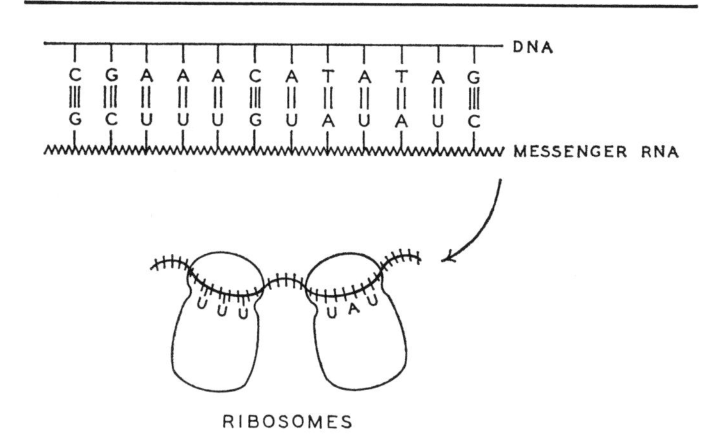

FIGURE 3. *A diagram showing how messenger ribonucleic acid (RNA) is produced upon the template provided by one strand of a DNA molecule, so that the bases in the messenger RNA are complementary to those in the DNA strand. Note that the base thymine which is found in DNA is replaced in RNA by a similar base, uracil (U), which pairs with adenine also. The messenger RNA, once formed, peels away from the DNA, leaves the nucleus of the cell, and becomes associated in the cytoplasm with certain protein-RNA bodies visible in electron micrographs, but too small to see in the ordinary microscope. A number of ribosomes are temporarily united, or held together, by a single strand of messenger RNA.*

RNA an entirely distinct function. Instead of replicating itself in the nucleus, it picks up a code message from the DNA master upon which it is laid down, transports the message to the ribosomes, and there forms a template or mold upon which the amino acid units that enter into the composition of a protein or polypeptide chain are brought together in the correct sequence. This over-simplified account is sufficient to bring out the point I wish to stress. The messenger-RNA molecules that serve as intermediaries between the genes and the enzymes must be stable in structure. Natural selection, working over eons of time since DNA and RNA first arose in living systems, has perfected an arrangement that is stable and efficient, remarkably proof against accidents, and yet one that can turn minor accidental changes in the sequence of the bases in these nucleic acids into variations of structure and function in the cells, variations that may occasionally prove advantageous in some new or changing environment. Clearly, the properties of the molecular level determine the adaptive capacities of the next level of living organization, the level of the cells.

The Cellular Level

Two aspects most strikingly characterize living cells. The first is their remarkable internal organization and harmonious integration of molecular systems. The second is the equally marvelous capacity of the cell to respond to external stimuli by making appropriate responses. It is at the level of the cell that we first see clearly the properties and characteristics of life.

In an average cell there are some thousands of controlled chemical processes, each of them mediated by a specific enzyme which itself must be properly put together on the surface of certain ribosomes. Twenty sorts of small RNA molecules carry twenty sorts of energized amino acid units to the sites of protein synthesis. Each sort of transfer-RNA, as it is called, delivers its amino acid load to a specific site corresponding to the right triplet of the code supplied by the messenger-RNA as it lies on the ribosome (Fig. 4). The amino acids, thus aligned in appropriate sequence, become chemically bonded into a polypeptide chain that is set free

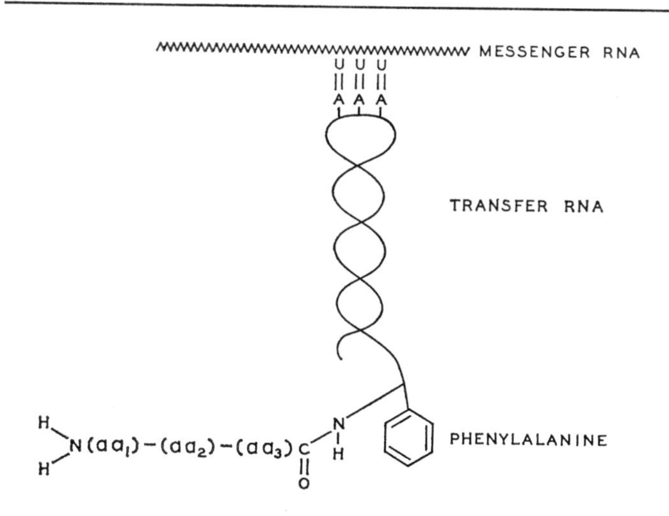

FIGURE 4. *A diagram showing how the messenger RNA, when associated with the ribosomes, serves as a basis for aligning the twenty or more kinds of transfer RNA molecules which bring the twenty commonly occurring kinds of amino acids into just the sequence needed in a particular polypeptide chain. One or more polypeptides compose each enzyme or structural protein.*

from the transfer-RNA and peels off from the ribosome. It is then ready to fold up into the right shape, or to unite with other polypeptides to form a composite unit; and thereafter it must be transported to the right place to fulfil its own function.

In another kind of body within the cell, respiration is going on. In these structures, known as mitochondria, fuel foods such as sugars and fats are broken down step by step and their energy trapped in a nucleotide which is like one of those present in RNA but carries extra phosphate groups attached

(Fig. 5). It is known as ATP, a contraction for adenosine triphosphate. This molecule, produced in the "powerhouse of the cell," its dozens or hundreds of collective mitochondria, supplies energy for all the numerous controlled reactions of the cell, including the synthesis of proteins on the ribosomes and the replication of the DNA within the nucleus. The steps in the breakdown of the sugar glucose, to take an example, are very numerous; and the enzymes engaged must, for the sake of efficiency, be lined up in order, like the workmen who perform successive steps on an assembly line in a factory. And all of this highly organized work in the powerhouses must be kept separate from all the other chemical activities in the rest of the cell that might interfere.

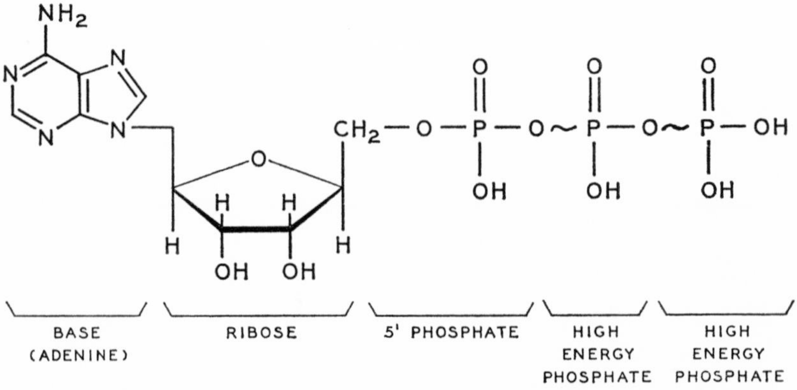

BASE (ADENINE) — RIBOSE — 5' PHOSPHATE — HIGH ENERGY PHOSPHATE — HIGH ENERGY PHOSPHATE

FIGURE 5. *The molecular structure of adenosine triphosphate, commonly called* ATP. *This nucleotide (a molecule composed of a united organic base, sugar, and phosphate) is the compound virtually universally used by living organisms for transferring energy from one chemical system to another.*

There are many other separate, organized bodies within the cell where different kinds of processes are carried out, but our present purposes are served if we merely note their existence. Collectively, they promote a harmonious interplay of enzyme-controlled systems and economy in the use of materials. But we must look at the problem of regulation more closely if we are to appreciate the nature of the adaptive fitness achieved by the cell. Even in a cell carrying on all of these hundreds of controlled activities, not all of them proceed at the same time. There may be a lull in protein synthesis at one moment, and a quickening of respiration at another. The cell divides periodically, after it has grown to sufficient size. Between divisions of the cell, its DNA must replicate. The duplicate chromosomes then become attached to a special structure that forms in the cell, a spindle, and on this spindle the strands of each chromosome separate. The two identical daughter chromosomes pass to opposite poles of the spindle; and each daughter cell receives not only an abundance of ribosomes and mitochondria and other essential structures, but a complete, representative set of all the chromosomes that were present in the parent cell. What regulates the timing of these processes? What co-ordinates them? How are the genes turned on and off?

The details of the regulatory mechanisms are known in only a few cases. Some of them involve feedbacks, producing either a positive enhancement of activity, or a negative, inhibitory effect. In some cases it is the chemical product of a reaction that inhibits production of one of the enzymes in the chain of steps leading to it. In other cases, the temporary combination of the enzyme with its own substrate produces an intermediate compound that stimulates the cell to produce additional amounts of enzyme. How is this brought about? Does the inhibitory or stimulatory substance act on the RNA at the site where the enzyme is synthesized? Or does it prevent the formation of the messenger-RNA by the gene involved? Or does it act even more directly, turning on or turning off the gene itself? At present we do not know. Nevertheless, it is evident that regulation does exist and that the cell makes this or that product according to its needs.

We have described only a part of the adaptive organization of the cell. As conditions change within it, activity is modified; but also, as conditions change outside it, it makes appropriate responses. It may contract, or move from one place to another; it may secrete some chemical product into the surroundings; it may emit light or generate an electric impulse. Every cell possesses the capacity to become aroused or excited in the face of stimuli and to vary its responses accordingly. The capacity to make suitable responses is important for the survival of the cell and is a part of the cell's genetic heritage. It is based on its supply of genes and chromosomes, its enzymes, its mitochondria, its ribosomes, and other structures. In a multicellular organism, such as most green plants and most animals, the cell's immediate environment consists of other cells. These establish, by their presence, the needs and conditions of the cell's life, and they supply the source of the excitations that alter the cell's condition and lead to its responses. The value of the cell's capacities is thus not merely intrinsic. They are relative to the cell's relations to all its neighbors.

Tissues and Organs

One of the most obvious and most significant of the changes that take place as a multicellular organism develops is the differentiation of its cells. They do not all remain alike. They become specialists. Each special type of cell sacrifices a certain degree of its general capacity to concentrate its efforts on a particular function, such as contraction, secretion, or the transmission of a nervous impulse. What this means is that the protein-making machinery of the cell becomes largely limited to the production of one or two kinds of protein. In the muscle cell we find chiefly actin and myosin; in the cartilage cell we find almost exclusively collagen; in the red blood cell mainly hemoglobin. With a high degree of specialization, the types of cells become respectively more and more efficient in their functions. But observe—as they become more specialized, they also become more dependent on each other. A jack-of-all-trades may live alone; but a carpenter must be a member of a society or he will starve. The specialized cells are grouped into tissues composed of thousands of similar cells—in unity there is strength. The tissues are in turn grouped into organs, each of which consists of a number of different tissues performing different functions individually, though one great function collectively. Thus the heart is made largely of special muscle cells; but this tissue is supplemented by the endothelial tissue that lines the heart cavities and forms the valves, by the elastin-forming cells, by the several tissues of the heart's own blood vessels, by nerve cells and other communicative cells that bond the individual contractions of the heart muscle into one co-ordinated beat and time them properly.

It is not necessary to labor the obvious. Here, as at the lower levels of organization, we find appropriate responses to external stimuli, a harmonious co-ordination and co-operation of cells, regulation and control. These qualities and capacities have value because they contribute to survival. Growth and development are increasingly important in the larger multicellular organisms, since the larger organisms have a greater opportunity for differentiation, and thereby a heightened efficiency. Yet, though the single cell may live alone, the heart and the stomach and the eye cannot live alone. They have no real meaning alone. They exist for the body of which they form a part. Their values are submerged in the values of the next higher level of living organization, the individual.

The Individual

The harmony of the body grows from the unity of its diverse parts. Their co-ordination is achieved on many levels. One of these is the molecular level, for cells from one person grafted into a person of a different genotype may at first appear to heal in place and to grow, but before long will be rejected. All of us are familiar, moreover, with the co-ordination achieved in the human body at the tissue and organ level through the mediation of nerves and hormones.

The subordination of the parts to the unity of the whole body of which they are members is a truism; what does it really signify? There is life in the cells, tissues, and organs, but so far as we know there is no individual consciousness of "self." Each organ responds appropriately to the nervous stimuli and chemical messengers it receives, in accordance with its nature. Its needs are met by the contributions of the other organs, but it is not made cheerful or content thereby, even though it may signal its increasing hunger or disturbance to the guidance centers of the body. One wonders, too, about the white blood cell, roving like an amoeba through the circulatory vessels of the body, penetrating into the tissue spaces, collecting where the body is being invaded by foreign organisms, and often sacrificing its own life in combat with the foe. Does it, in these actions, recognize its nature as part of a greater whole, as belonging to the body it is defending? If we say "No" because the leucocyte has no apparent means of thought, what then do we say of the cancer cell, which originates from the same stem-cells as the other cells of the body, but which nevertheless loses its identity with the body, and becomes a predatory tissue that lives for itself alone, sapping the strength of the very tissues on which it depends for further existence and killing the very body that gave it life?

The behavior of the individual organism exhibits internally a remarkable homeostasis, or ability to maintain its internal environment constant. Externally its behavior in response to stimuli from the environment takes on the forms of reflex response, instinct, and learning. In making appropriate adjustments to the environment each of these has its own special value. The reflex response provides a quick, automatic response—such as the blink of an eye or the jerk of a hand away from contact with a hot object. The reflex does not need to be learned. Its survival value is readily apparent.

Instincts, being inborn, are products of the genes through the normal paths of development. These behavior patterns are relatively rigid and unmodifiable; but in an environment that is sufficiently stable to permit the instinct to function properly there is great value in the possession of a type of behavior that, like a reflex, need not be learned, but that, like learned behavior, may be complex. Learned behavior, by contrast, offers no such promise of always providing a successful adjustment, especially in the early stages of learning; but it is far more flexible in the face of varying environmental demands. In general, instinct and learning occupy inversely related portions of the total behavior. In insects there is great dependence upon instinct and very little learning. In mammals there is much dependence upon learning and rather little upon instinct. But both probably exist in all species, and they are often blended nicely. For example, the singing of a songbird is both. Young birds have been isolated in cages where they cannot ever have heard any other bird sing, and they begin to sing instinctively; but the particular song that is characteristic of a species must be learned by imitation, for these isolated young birds do not develop the typical song of their species.

The harmony of the body, its homeostasis, and its reflex, instinctive, and learned behavior, all have survival value for the individual, all contribute to viability. They all point down to the lower levels of organization on which they are based. Yet, as we began by saying, the individual does not live forever. Reproduction points not only to the future, offering new opportunities for new genotypes to be tested out in new environments, and entailing death for the older generation of beings—it also points to the higher levels of biological organization. Evolutionary values are not merely those restricted to the survival of individuals. That is less important, in the end, than survival of the species, the community, and the biome.

The Population

Individuals, especially in sexually reproducing species, belong to a population within which interbreeding of various genetic types may occur; and the species is made up of one or more such populations. At this level of biological organization seemingly quite new relationships and values intrude. The populations are not static. Whenever an empty niche occurs in the habitat, it is invaded by the nearest populations. If the habitat permits a number of different ways of life, and these are not pre-empted, the incoming population will differentiate very rapidly—in evolutionary terms—into types adapted to these different ways of life. The adaptive radiation of the Galapagos finches was one of the startling phenomena that made Charles Darwin awaken to the possibility of an origin of new species. The marsupial mammals of Australia, so long isolated from the rest of the world, and likewise those of South America, underwent an even greater long-term diversification. Progressive adaptation in relation to the available environments is the general rule.

The survival and continuity of the populations and species seem often to depend upon the rise of some form of social order, representing a mutual dependence of individuals upon one another. In its simplest form this social grouping is the family, composed of the mother (and sometimes the father too), and the young ones during the dependent stage of their growth and development. The great insect societies are only extended broods or families of this kind. A step beyond is the herd, or tribe, composed of many families banded together for common protection. No animal but man has achieved the still fuller extension of this banding together to make a real society. Insects, especially the ants and the termites, have evolved family organizations in which there are many castes, or types of specialized workers. Only in human society do we find specialized individuals basing their skills upon learning rather than instinct. Mutually satisfactory relations between the individuals in a society based on learning must be fostered by education and must be guarded by law. The values inherent in co-operation and co-ordination, promoted so blindly but so perfectly on the level of the cell by the chemical organization it possesses, promoted so perfectly and so blindly in the insect society by their inherited instincts and their mutual recognition of their fellows, must in the society which is based on learning be imposed by force or be nurtured by conscience. Religion that exalts these values, that declares that "all men are brothers," and invokes the force of human kindness and of brotherly love to cement these bonds, clearly plays a great part in the preservation of this type of society.

The Community

Every habitat is populated by numerous kinds of living organisms. Because they unavoidably affect one another, they form a community. The animals could not live without the plants, for they either feed upon them directly, or prey upon other animals which are plant-eaters. The green plants in their photosynthesis withdraw carbon dioxide from the atmosphere and return to the air an abundant supply of oxygen; the animals breathe up the oxygen and return their carbon dioxide to the atmosphere. Nitrogen moves in a great cycle from the air into the soil, where nitrogen-fixing bacteria, many of them living within nodules on the roots of legumes, convert the gaseous nitrogen to nitrates. These the plants can use to synthesize amino acids. Animals, which cannot synthesize amino acids, eat the plants, obtain the amino acids, and synthesize them into proteins. As the older generations of plants and animals die, their proteins decay. Soil bacteria, the ultimate decomposers, produce ammonia from these proteins and from the nitrogenous wastes of living organisms. The ammonia may escape into the air, but much of it is converted by other bacteria into nitrites and then into nitrates, which are once more available for plants to absorb and utilize. Water, carbon, hydrogen, mineral elements, all move in similar cycles and make all creatures interdependent.

The mutual relations are often much closer than those just described. All grades of living together, or "symbiosis" as the biologist calls it, can be found. A little fish lives among the protective spines of a sea urchin. A hermit crab places a sea anemone on its claw. A tick-bird pulls the parasites from the leathery hide of a rhinoceros. An ant colony grows a garden of protected fungus in its nest on beds of carefully selected leaves. A fungus and an alga completely lose their independent identity in becoming a lichen growing on a rock in the sun, on the bark of a tree, or on the snowy tundra. Some insects become completely dependent upon the plants they pollinate, and the plants become completely dependent upon their insect aides for successful reproduction. The yucca and the yucca moth, the fig and the fig wasp, are but two of many such examples. This chapter of natural history is one of the most fascinating. It could readily be expanded to fill a dozen volumes. Here we can do no more than name these few in order to illustrate the harmony that develops in the members of a mutualism. In structure and in behavior, in their chemistry and in their genes, such partners become so interrelated that they are as truly a unit as the members of a family or a society belonging to a single species.

The interrelationships are not always so pleasant to contemplate. In this same chapter of the book of nature we meet with predators and their hapless prey, with parasites and their helpless hosts. Disease stalks these pages, and cruel and bloody death is her companion. Life must live at the expense of life. These were the thoughts that drove T. H. Huxley to despair when he considered the nature of evolution, that made Darwin disconsolate, as he wrote to Asa Gray: "There seems to me too much misery in the world. I cannot persuade myself that a beneficent and omnipotent God would have designedly created the Ichneumonidae with the express intention of their feeding within the living bodies of caterpillars, or that a cat should play with mice." [4]

Even here the studies of the past century have cast a clearer light. The parasite that kills its host deprives itself of bed and

4. Francis Darwin. *The Life and Letters of Charles Darwin* (New York and London: D. Appleton and Company, 1925), Volume II, p. 105.

board. It is not so well adjusted to its environment as the parasite that can live without causing its host too great a loss of vigor or too great discomfort. If natural selection provides a basis for continuous progressive adaptation, the virulent agent of disease may be seen as an organism at the beginning of the road leading to some form of mutualism, rather than as an ultimate evil. Predators, too, have come to be recognized as being usually very necessary for the well-being of the population and species on which they prey. In Arizona, after most of the wolves, coyotes, and mountain lions had been killed, the deer population multiplied beyond the bounds of the available food supply, and in some winters thousands of them have died miserably of starvation.

A classic story to illustrate this point is that of the moose and the wolves on Isle Royale in Lake Superior. When the moose first gained access to the island, in a winter when the lake froze over between the island and the mainland, they found a virtual moose paradise—plenty of food and no wolves. They multiplied year by year until the moose population had stripped the bark from all the young trees and devoured the winter food supply. Then they began to die of famine. The rangers introduced some wolves from a zoo, but these were so civilized they preferred to stay around the camp and to eat garbage rather than engage in the arduous business of hunting moose. They had to be trapped and returned to the zoo, except for one which successfully avoided the traps. Eventually, in an unusually severe winter, the lake froze over again, and on this occasion a wolf pack made its way across to the island. The wolves began hunting the over-abundant moose, killing the weakest and most malnourished. Today, the populations of moose, and also of wolves, have become mutually adjusted, and the island supports a stable population of about 300 moose and 25 wolves. It is clear that while individual moose may die because of the presence of wolves, the continued well-being of the moose population and in the long run its evolutionary advances in adaptation depend upon the existence of the moose's predators. Swiftness in running, great size and strength, horns and antlers, and many less evident features of anatomy and physiology are produced through the selection pressure exerted by predators. The obverse of the coin is the development of larger size and greater strength, swiftness and cunning, improved claws and teeth, and social habits of hunting in the predatory animals. As the prey improves its defenses and means of escape in the evolutionary process, the predator, pari passu, is forced by selection to make compensatory advances. Neither evolves as it does without the other, any more than the squirrel would have become what it is without trees bearing nuts, or than the trees would have become nut trees in the absence of animals like squirrels.

The Biome

Seen broadly, all life is interknit and mutually interdependent. Though individual species may become extinct, just as the individual organisms of one generation die and are supplanted by those with novel genotypes, the evolution of all organic nature must be viewed as a single process, an indissoluble whole of which we gain only an imperfect idea by examining scraps and patches. The positive value of a successful adaptation or the negative value of an inborn metabolic error, from our human bias, relates to the survival of the individual and the transmission of his characteristics to later generations. But the relativity of values, so clearly seen in respect to differences of place, applies also to differences of time and to differences of level. What is so keenly desired by the individual, namely, his survival, may be extended in us to include a desire for personal immortality. The selection of the genotype has endowed all sentient life with an instinct of self-preservation; but it has also endowed individuals with a limited life span, characteristic for each species and related to its mortality from accident and disease, its fertility and reproductive pattern, and the available subsistence and living space. It is no accident that the longest-lived species of mammals, for example, are the ones with the lowest fecundity and the greatest need on the part of the young for care. Yet conflict arises as the desire of the individual to live clashes with the need of the species, of the community, and of the entire biome for the individual to die. It seems to me that too much weight has been given in the discussion of the nature of natural selection and its effects to the value of *survival* and not enough to the value of *death*.

CONCLUSION: GOOD AND EVIL

Our analysis leads us to the conclusion that the process of organic evolution certainly involves values, inasmuch as there is a constant struggle between the better and the worse for perpetuation. These values can be measured quantitatively, by measuring survival and perpetuation at different levels, such as the frequencies of alternative genes, the frequencies of competing genotypes of individuals, or the numbers of individuals in competing species. But these values are always relative. They become altered in measure as the environment becomes altered. They increase or diminish, or even change sign altogether, as one shifts attention from one level of biological organization to another. From the standpoint of the gene's own perpetuation, that state is best which is most immutable. But from the standpoint of the species in an evolving biome, that gene is best which is mutable yet not too mutable, one with its mutability regulated at a level that in each generation of individuals provides just a few altered genes. What that means is in turn relative to the size of the population and also relative, of course, to the nature of reproduction, sexual or asexual.

No human mind has yet succeeded in integrating all of these values, nor is any computer ready to cope with the problem, since we do not know what to feed into the machine in the way of information. Nevertheless, as human beings we can surely recognize that the scales and mutations of values far transcend our immediate subjective human desires. Our desires are necessarily limited because we stand at one point in the scale of biological organization, wilfully subordinating all values at levels below our own individuality to the values of the individual, and closing our eyes to the values that apply on higher levels of organization. Now we must endeavor—and let us hope in sufficient time, before the human species has completely destroyed the entire biosphere—to understand these values throughout the entire scale of life.

In the second and third chapters of Genesis is the story of the Garden of Eden and the Fall of Man. Too much dust has been stirred by debates about its historicity, for in such controversy the deeper moral truths the story reveals usually lie forgotten. The tree whose fruit Man was forbidden to eat was not the Tree of Life. It was the Tree of Knowledge of Good and Evil. For indeed, in his ignorance, man was once innocent. Yet "when, in the agelong evolutionary ascent, man came to foresee the consequences of at least some of his actions, when he could distinguish the good from the evil and the better from the worse, then it became to him sin to choose the evil, to do the worse." [5] The dawn of conscience,

5. Bentley Glass. *Science and Liberal Education* (Baton Rouge: Louisiana State University Press, 1959), p. 114.

like so many ages earlier the origin of pain, marked the commencement of an era of new and wider recognition of consequences, and hence of values above, beyond, and beneath our individual desires.

In this analysis I have dealt only with biological, evolutionary values. I have not discussed the question of whether other values, peculiar to man or absolute in nature, may exist. What I have clarified, I hope, is the greater, broader scope of these biological values than most persons are willing to recognize or acknowledge. As we examine the progressive adaptations of evolving life, at all levels of organization, and as the evolutionary values become clearer to us, one thing is certain. We cannot turn the clock back. We cannot regain the Garden of Eden or recapture our lost innocence. From now on we are responsible for the welfare of all living things, and what we do will mold or shatter our own heart's desire.

2

HUMAN HEREDITY AND THE ETHICS OF TOMORROW

Our systems of values might be viewed from a biological, evolutionary viewpoint only, as in the previous essay. Yet social and cultural values, moral absolutes, and human ethics must also be considered. I propose next to examine some of the problems of human heredity in order to see what light may be thrown on questions of human values by means of a biological analysis in a special field, one that inescapably intrudes upon social and cultural values, provokes new standards of ethics, and clashes with moral absolutes.

It has frequently been said that the definition of values in evolutionary terms involves purely circular reasoning. "The survival of the fittest" requires some definition and measurement of "fitness"; but fitness can be defined and measured only in terms of survival. Even if we add the more modern emphasis on differential fertility, we do not seem to escape the circularity. Yet the difficulty is more apparent than real, for the charge of circularity of reasoning ignores the progressive nature of evolutionary adaptation, its dynamic characteristic. It would be better to say: "The evolutionary advances of each generation are made on the basis of the survivors and reproducers of the generation before." Instead of a circular image, we may instead think of a coil or helix, upon which movement in a full circle brings one back not to the starting-point but to one above it.

The human genotypes of today are enormously varied. They include both individual and racial differences. Collectively they are also undoubtedly different from the genotypes of Neanderthal man and his contemporaries, and even more different from those of Pithecanthropus and earlier human species. These differences rest upon the steady process of change resulting from the occurrence of mutations, the elimination of most of them, and the preservation in the gene pool of this or that population of just a few. It is indeed true of mutations to say: "Many shall be called, but few chosen."

The effect of a particular mutation is not always the same. Other genes, known as modifiers, are numerous and may alter the expression of a gene almost or quite beyond recognition. Some modifiers may enhance, some may suppress. In this respect, a gene is known by the company it keeps. Natural selection, then, is never able to act upon a single gene. It can eliminate only the entire genotype of an individual that fails to reproduce, and in this way eliminate the faulty gene. It is therefore only on the average, in a very large statistical manner, that detrimental genes become eliminated and other genes are preserved. If the genotype as a whole is perpetuated, as in fact is the case in ordinary cell division and in asexual reproduction, the gene that might do better in a different company of other genes never gets the chance.

In asexual reproduction, mutations occurring in any particular individual may be transmitted to all of that individual's progeny, but all the progeny remain alike in genotype. Mutations that occur in different individuals or lines of descent have no chance of getting together. Let us suppose—what is by no means uncommon—that a mutation from A to *A′* is detrimental and a mutation from *B* to *B′* is also detrimental; but that the genotype *A′B′* would, if it could be formed, be superior in selective quality to the original genotype *AB*. In asexual reproduction there is virtually no way in which this desirable genotype *A′B′* can arise. For if the frequency of mutation from A to *A′* is one per million and the frequency of mutation of *B* to *B′* is one per million and the two mutations are completely independent in occurrence—as is the general rule—then the probability that both will occur in the same individual is no more than one per million million, that is, one per trillion (10^{-12}). On the other hand, if either the mutation A to *A′* or *B* to *B′* occurs first, it will in all probability be eliminated before the mutant individual multiplies to a million offspring and there is a reasonable chance that the other mutation will occur in the same lineage.

To speak teleologically, nature invented sex to get around this difficulty. In sexual reproduction, the cellular events which involve the chromosomes—the bearers of the genes—include two main steps. First, there is a selection of a single set of chromosomes from the two sets present in the cell. The single set comprises one chromosome of each kind, irrespective of whether each particular chromosome was originally inherited from the male or female parent of the individual. Second, there is a fusion of one sex cell from the male with a sex cell from the female. The first of these phases of the sexual process, called meiosis, provides a vast number of reproductive cells, that is, of eggs or sperms, with almost illimitable possibilities of random assortment of different alternative genes derived from the male parent or the female parent. For example, if the genotype of the individual is *AA′*; *BB′*, the reproductive cells may carry [*A*;*B*] or [*A*;*B′*] or [*A′*;*B*] or [*A′*;*B′*]. The second process, fertilization, reassembles the chromosomes and their genes in pairs. The immediate consequence is that a fresh mutant *A′* or *B′* gene is accompanied by a normal A or *B* gene, and its detrimental effect is wholly or partially masked. Hence it can be transmitted to many offspring, so that the population will at length contain many carriers of *A′* or *B′* before any harm is done. As a result of fertilization, the fertilized egg may have any combination of genes producible by the random meeting of all kinds of sperms with all kinds of eggs available in the particular mating. Thus, if there are 10,000 pairs of genes in a certain species, and in a particular mating there are mutant genes at 1 per cent of these loci in each parent, each parent will be capable of producing 2^{100} genetically different kinds of reproductive cells; and random fertilization is then capable of producing $(2^{100})^2$ kinds of offspring.[1] This not extreme assumption with respect to the presence of mutant genes illustrates what an infinite variety of hereditary types can arise from even a single pair of sexually reproducing organisms. Thus, if one parent is *AA′;BB* and the other *AA;BB′*, there is a possibility—a probability of one out of four—that the offspring will carry the combination of *A′* with *B′*, the lucky combination that was virtually impossible in the case of asexual reproduction.

The fertilized human egg contains 46 chromosomes, 23 of them inherited from the egg, 23 of them inherited from the sperm. The number of different genotypes that might be present in a single fertilized egg, if there were only 23 differences between the genes in the two sets of chromosomes in the father, and 23 other differences between the genes in the two sets of chromosomes in the mother, i.e., one difference per pair of chromosomes, would be $(2^{23})^2$. That is to say, the mother could potentially produce 2^{23}, or 8,388,608 genetically different sorts of eggs, and the father an equal number of sperms with different genotypes. Hence there is a possibility through random fertilization of nearly 70 trillion genotypes of offspring. That would amount to about 2,300 generations of the entire present population of the entire world.

In some persons there may be fewer than 23 differences between the maternally and the paternally inherited genes occupying identical locations in homologous chromosomes. But even if there were only 10 differences between the genes in the father and only the same 10 differences in the mother,

1. This number, 2^{200}, is a billion times greater than the number of atoms making up the earth.

there would still be nearly 60,000 possible different genotypes among the offspring. All this amounts to saying that the variety of human genotypes is essentially inexhaustible, that there is only an infinitesimal chance that any two persons, whether born of the same or different parents, will be identical in all genetic respects. There is one exception: identical twins, triplets, quadruplets, or quintuplets who arise by splitting of the same fertilized egg or embryo. Unless you chance to be one of these, you are unique in human history. Yet even that is not so important, since you may still resemble certain other individuals in all except a few minor ways. The crucial fact is that all this potential variation in genotypes exists in every generation. The genotypes do not remain intact. The harmful genes and the beneficial genes become reassorted into new genotypes, upon which natural selection may act forthwith. Exactly the genotype best suited to some new alteration of the environment may arise before it is too late—before the entire population has been exterminated.

The genes, through their control of the chemical machinery of life, govern the processes and potentialities of development. No one actually inherits blue eyes or red hair, for the fertilized egg is nothing but a single cell. It has no eyes and no hair, only certain genes in its nucleus and certain organized enzyme systems in its cytoplasm. Therefore we are clearly dealing only with the inheritance of potentialities. Potentialities, of course, depend for their realization on many things outside, as well as inside, the forming individual. Some characteristics, if the embryo can live and develop at all, turn out to be modified very little by the vicissitudes of the environment. Others may be altered radically or may be suppressed altogether. For example, one's ABO blood group depends upon certain substances formed on the red blood cells during prenatal development, and no one has found any way to change a person's blood group. It is less modifiable than one's fingerprints. On the other hand one's dental conformation may be altered considerably by wearing dental braces; one's natural weight may be changed materially by over-eating; one's intelligence may be stunted by isolation from one's fellows and deprivation of normal activities. The case is the same as in our experimental fruit flies, some of which have curly wings under all conditions of development, some of which always have flat wings, and some of which have a gene that produces curly wings if the development takes place at a temperature above 16°C and flat wings if it takes place at a lower temperature.

Suppose one asks, then, just what are the potentialities of a particular genotype? The answer can only be secured through the experiment of testing out the genotype in a variety of conditions. If one can secure many individuals with the same, or very nearly the same, genotype the experiment can be made. We can do this with fruit flies or mice or peas. But if all human beings are genetically different from all others, the experiment is simply impossible. What we can do, however, is to provide "standard" or "ideal" conditions for the development of every individual, and then appraise the significance of the genetic differences. Until then, we simply cannot say whether any differences we observe are basically hereditary. And even then, we cannot say whether under different "standard" conditions the ranking might not be quite altered. The genetic basis for the development of a young Mozart might exist in two infants, one growing up in Salzburg and the other in a mountain tribe in interior New Guinea. To guess the outcome will not strain the imagination of anyone.

The tremendous advances of humanity in material power

during the very short period, in evolutionary perspective, of less than 10,000 years, the development of distinct cultures, and the even more phenomenal transformation of human conditions in the past 400 years, since the beginning of modern science and technological invention, cannot possibly have involved much change in the basic human gene pool which existed at the beginning of civilization. Natural selection works slowly to produce change. A new species of mammal may take on the average 5 million years to arise, George Gaylord Simpson has estimated. A new primate species may take somewhat less, at least during Pleistocene times. Modern man has been on the earth for an immense stretch of time—at least 40,000 years, and maybe several hundred thousand—without much change in his skeletal anatomy. We are therefore justified, I think, in regarding all this tremendous human advance in culture and civilization, in material power and relative understanding of nature, as having occurred with little if any genetic change. Cro-Magnon man was probably about as intelligent as most of us today. He possessed great technical skill in making flint tools. His artistry in painting and sculpture was remarkable, and almost unsurpassed until the Renaissance. The great advances made by modern man therefore reflect no change in his biological heritage but represent a new phenomenon, the advent of cultural transmission, the accumulation of knowledge and its transfer from one generation to the next. This transmission has sometimes been called cultural inheritance, and analogies and parallels with biological inheritance have been drawn, from the time of Herbert Spencer until now. Yet it may not be very profitable to do so. The differences between cultural and genetic inheritance may be more profound than the similarities. There is nothing in education, or in cultural inheritance, that corresponds to the genotype of the individual, nothing that corresponds to the reshuffling and recombination of the genetic material in meiosis and fertilization, nothing that corresponds very well to the role of natural selection on the gene pool. On the other hand, biological inheritance lacks anything to match the more and more rapid accumulation of knowledge, the exponential growth of science, the extension of powers and adaptations beyond the individual.

In one major respect the two kinds of inheritance are nevertheless alike. Both of them represent potentialities which the individual must develop, and in both cases the environment enhances or limits the realization of those potentialities. In the present civilized world, a good genetic endowment is requisite to the full enjoyment of the cultural heritage; a good cultural environment is needed for the development and realization of the genetic potentialities. This amounts to saying that precise estimation of the genetic worth of an individual requires an optimum environment for his development, and that is why the geneticist, fully recognizing the differences between individuals and races, demands equal opportunity for all.

Theodosius Dobzhansky has recently written that "genetic diversity is mankind's most precious resource, not a regrettable deviation from an ideal state of monotonous sameness." [2] On the other hand, H. J. Muller has stoutly advocated applying positive genetic selection to human reproduction, with the aim of improving our genetic heritage in the direction of many indubitably fine qualities.[3] Is there a contradiction here? One might suspect that any use of a few

2. Th. Dobzhansky. 1962. Genetics and equality. *Science*, 137: 112.

3. H. J. Muller, "The Guidance of Human Evolution," in Sol Tax, ed., *The Evolution of Man* (Evolution after Darwin, Vol. II) (Chicago: University of Chicago Press, 1960), pp. 423–62.

selected male sires to produce, by artificial insemination, a large number of offspring might tend to decrease human diversity and might possibly produce a new caste system, which Dobzhansky has called "the grandest genetic experiment ever attempted with human materials" and then termed "a failure, in the sense that the castes have not become genetically specialized for their respective occupations." [4] Nevertheless, I would suspect that the reshuffling and recombination of the genes in the reproductive process is so great that extreme similarity would not be expected. Half-sibs are not in general much alike, and if in addition they were reared in different homes or institutions, they would differ almost as much as individuals picked at random from the population. A ban on the inbreeding of near descendants of a common sire might have to be enforced with some vigor. Muller has himself recognized this danger, and in his latest proposals to use selected sperm donors for eugenic improvement of the population would limit to twenty the offspring of any single sire.

Equal opportunity must be coupled with freedom of the individual if it is to lead to fullest development of the potential of the genotype. A social system that keeps an individual of high potential in the class of "hewers of wood and drawers of water," as the caste system in India undertook to do, limits by restriction of the environment the development of a person's full potential. If the genotype of the human being was like that of an ant, based largely on instinct rather than learning, castes and restricted freedom and opportunity would be all very well. But mastery of our cultural inheritance and its further extension require the fullest development of the potentialities of each individual, and this

4. Dobzhansky, *op. cit.*, p. 113.

cannot be done without freedom of the individual to seek and find his own select environment.

THE ETHICS OF THE GENE POOL

New ethical problems arise as our knowledge of the composition of the gene pools of our several populations increases and we discern the factors of change that alter their composition. Knowledge creates responsibility.

Ethical Problems of Mutation

As we have learned more about mutations and how they may be induced, a host of new dangers arise to threaten us and create fear. The gene pool at the present time already contains many detrimental mutant genes. Most of them are fortunately recessive. Recent estimates by more than one method indicate that each of us, on the average, carries four to eight recessive lethal genes, or their equivalent in larger numbers of less drastic forms of mutation. Approximately 4 per cent of all births bear tangible evidence of genetic defect, mainly as a consequence of the conjunction in one individual of two doses of the same defective gene. Any increase in the average mutation rate of the genes in the gene pool above current spontaneous levels will automatically increase the number of defective births. Thus a permanent doubling of the mutation rate will lead eventually to a doubled frequency of genetically defective births. With a social burden of about 160,000 genetically defective babies born annually in the United States alone, it is a matter of real consequence to avoid any increase in the mutation rate.

The study of the mutation process over the past 35 years has revealed three classes of environmental agents capable of producing mutations in the genes of the reproductive cells:

(1) ionizing radiations and ultraviolet rays; (2) increased temperature, or temperature shocks; and (3) a variety of chemical agents, but especially those which react with the purine or pyrimidine bases of deoxyribonucleic acid (DNA). The hazards posed by each of these types of mutation-inducing agents may be considered briefly.

Ultraviolet rays penetrate so slightly that for human beings they present no danger of producing mutations in the reproductive cells. They are absorbed entirely in the skin. Ionizing radiations, having a far greater penetrating power, are another matter. Cosmic rays, gamma rays from radium or other radioactive substances, beta rays (or electrons), X-rays, and high-energy particles such as beams of alpha particles, neutrons, or protons, will both fracture chromosomes and alter the chemical structure of the DNA. The effects are scattered virtually at random through the genetic material. The mutations produced are of the most defective and detrimental kind. Relatively more chromosome breaks and lethals are produced by ionizing radiation than by most other mutagenic agents. Consequently, of all sources of mutation, high-energy radiation is the most serious and the most rigorously to be avoided, in so far as possible.

There is of course some ionizing radiation in our normal environment: the cosmic rays that increase in intensity and number with altitude, radiation from rocks and soil and building materials, radiation in the food we eat and the water we drink. The background radiation, as this is called, varies in amount from place to place. Over most of the United States it averages about 3 roentgens (the roentgen is the unit of X-ray dosage) spread over the first 30 years of life, a span of time chosen as being the average length of a human generation. That dose is about two to five times the gonadal dose received from a single fluoroscopy involving the pelvic region of the body, or about two to three times the total dose from all diagnostic X-rays received by the average member of the U.S. population up to the age of 30 years. In some parts of the United States, e.g., at high altitudes or wherever the drinking water is relatively high in radioactivity, or where the rock, soil, and building materials of the locality are igneous rock in origin, the background radiation may be as high as 5 roentgens accumulated in 30 years' time.

All genetic experiments ever conducted, including one conducted in my own laboratory with a dose of no more than 5 roentgens, indicate that there is direct linear proportionality between the dose of radiation administered and the frequency of mutations induced. The slope of the increase is different for different sorts of radiation and for different rates of administration, but for any given kind of radiation and specified dose rate, the linear relationship holds. There is no sign of a threshold below which mutations are not induced by high-energy radiations. These facts mean that the total dose accumulated by the reproductive organs from conception of the parent to conception of the offspring, and the integrated dose rate of all exposures, slow or fast, are the two parameters that determine the mutation frequency. Every dose, no matter how small, may be expected to have an effect proportional to its magnitude.

Medical diagnostic and therapeutic exposures to X-rays, radium, or other radioactive materials fall into the class of exposures at high dose rates, and they are therefore more damaging than exposures to the same number of roentgens at lower dose rates. Exposures of a chronic type, such as those from radioactive material that is ingested and remains temporarily, or even permanently, in the body, is usually at a low dose rate. This would apply to the radioactive fallout from weapons tests, for example. The radioactive isotopes strontium-90 and cesium-137 have long half-lives of approximately 30 years, but their residence time in the body is likely to be considerably shorter. The strontium-90, being chemically like calcium, is chiefly deposited in bone, where its weakly penetrating beta radiation is unable to reach the reproductive organs, although capable of doing local injury to the bone cells. There is recent evidence, however, that some strontium-90 enters the chromosomes themselves.[5] The cesium-137 produces gamma rays as well as beta rays and is more generally distributed in the body, so that gonadal radiation from fallout comes largely from this source. Fortunately, it does not stay so long in the body as the strontium-90 does. Iodine-131 is a short-lived radioactive product of atomic explosions. It is usually first to appear in quantity in food and milk after an explosion. Because it is concentrated almost entirely in the thyroid gland, the damage from its radioactivity is, like that of strontium-90, local, and it is very unlikely to produce genetic mutations in the reproductive cells.

The fallout on the United States from all weapons tests conducted through 1958 is estimated to have administered a gonadal dose averaging 0.1 roentgen per person. A similar amount has been added since 1961, making a total of 0.2 roentgen. From the standpoint of the individual person, it really does not matter that some persons have received gonadal doses considerably above that amount, while the majority of persons received rather less. Because most mutations are recessive, the damage done by new detrimental mutations is usually delayed for many generations, until eventually two descendants of the person in whom the mutation arose marry and have a child who inherits a double

5. K. G. Lüning, H. Frölen, A. Nelson, and C. Rönnbäck. 1963. Genetic effects of strontium-90 injected into male mice. *Nature*, 197: 304–5.

dose of the defective gene. The probability that harm will be done to the immediate offspring of an exposed person is probably not more than 10 per cent of the total damage the mutant gene will do in the population before it is eventually eliminated because of the early death or failure to reproduce of its bearers. Geneticists are therefore more concerned about the effects on the population as a whole of any general increase in abundance of harmful genes than they are about the doses received by particular individuals. It is the average dose to the reproductive organs of the entire population that matters most.

The crucial fact about exposure to fallout is that, while other man-made exposures to high-energy radiations are controlled as to dose and are limited to particular individuals, the fallout, like the rain and snow with which it descends to the earth's surface, falls on everybody. It is therefore like an addition to the natural background radiation. If we knew—as unfortunately we do not—exactly what proportion of all the spontaneous mutations that occur are attributable to background radiation, we could then estimate precisely the genetic mutation and damage done by the fallout. As matters stand, we can only estimate the consequences by using the relations between dose and mutation frequency obtained in experiments with animals, such as mice and fruit flies. Most of those experimental studies employed high dose rates, and the effects of the fallout should actually be about one-third of what was calculated in this way. We do know that for nearly all organisms a dose falling in the range between 40 and 80 roentgens doubles the number of mutations arising spontaneously. For example, in my own experiments with a dose of 5 r administered to fruit flies of both sexes, the doubling dose was 60 roentgens. There is some reason to expect, theoretically, that the doubling dose in human beings may be less rather than greater, but we cannot be sure. At low dose rates the doubling dose may be higher. The fallout to date, then, perhaps amounts to 0.25 or 0.5 per cent of a doubling dose. We have already stated that for the United States a doubling of the mutation rate would produce some 160,000 additional genetically handicapped births annually. The fallout would add to this number perhaps 400 to 800 per year, not a large proportion, but a matter of heartbreak to twice that many parents, and a considerable social and economic burden on the community. And remember, this is a minimum or very conservative estimate.

The ethical problem of the genetic effects of fallout has not been touched upon up to this point in the discussion. The populations of the United States, the NATO countries, the U.S.S.R. and its satellites may of course be expected to be willing, for the most part, to pay the price of genetic damage to some of their people, especially since it is postponed for many generations, in order to purchase greater immediate national security. The only question of ethics involved here is the right of one generation to secure something it wants at a price that must be paid by its descendants. Yet I wonder what would happen to our credit business if it were possible to purchase real estate and consumer's goods today and postpone payment until it fell upon our grandchildren?

The gravest ethical question in respect to fallout grows from the fact that the radioactive products of large nuclear explosions spread around the world in the stratosphere, and descend on the populations of nations that have resolved to take no part in the counter-alignments of East and West. It is simple justice that most of the fallout has in fact descended in the northern hemisphere and within the latitudes occupied by the very countries engaged in weapons tests, so that the American and Russian populations are in fact subjected to the greatest exposures. Populations living south of the equator have received less than half as much, but then only about one-tenth of the world's population does lie, at present, in the southern hemisphere. Plain arithmetic permits a conclusion that about sixteen times as many genetically defective infants will be born in the entire world as a result of fallout, as in the United States, or a total of 6,400 to 12,800 annually, at least three-fourths of them in populous countries of the world (such as India) not directly involved in the present nuclear alignment.

There is much talk about "clean bombs." It is true that weapons have been made in which the proportion of atomic fission has been greatly reduced and the proportion of fusion greatly increased; and these bombs produce much less of the radioactive isotopes we have been considering, strontium-90, iodine-131, and cesium-137. But the hydrogen fusion bombs generate carbon-14, a radioactive isotope with a half-life of thousands of years. Eminent geneticists have estimated that the genetic defects resulting from carbon-14 over all future generations may be twice as many as those resulting from the other fallout.

The ethical problem is thus two-headed. Have we the right to inflict damage on future generations for a present benefit? And have we the right to inflict damage on our neighbors who are bystanders in the political conflict? In a local community, if a homeowner burns foul-smelling refuse in his incinerator and it blows into his neighbors' houses, or if he produces a hazard to the general health of the neighborhood, the neighbors call the police. In international affairs, might still makes right—but should it? And is there no moral difference between injuring one's neighbor unwittingly and injuring him by doing knowingly that which will harm him? What a flagrant violation of the "Good Neighbor" policy! In a life-

and-death struggle much may be pardoned, but is it not necessary for us to end the offense as soon as can be? It is my personal opinion that this moral obligation has not weighed as it should in the consideration of a permanent weapons test ban. There is too much self-justification on the ground that only a little harm will be done to other peoples and that it will be spread out almost imperceptibly over the generations. A pathological fear of Soviet dishonesty and trickery has made us specious and dishonest on our part. This road may lead America to world tyranny. It cannot lead to true world leadership or world peace.

Before leaving the subject of mutation, something must be added about temperature and chemical mutagenic agents. Because of our homeostatically controlled body temperatures, human beings are less likely than plants and invertebrate animals or cold-blooded vertebrates to be subject to fluctuations of body temperature that might induce mutations. However, mention should be made of an interesting experimental study made a couple of years ago by a Swedish geneticist, Lars Ehrenberg, and his associates.[6] Thinking about the five-fold increase in mutation frequency observed in the fruit fly Drosophila and in micro-organisms when the temperature is raised by 10°C, Ehrenberg was led to wonder about the effect of clothing on the temperature of the relatively exposed male gonads, the testes. With delicate thermocouples he tested the scrotal temperatures of a sufficient number of nude men and a like number wearing their usual trousers. The testicular temperature averaged 3.3°C higher in the men wearing trousers! Now if temperature has the same mutagenic effect in humans as in lower

6. L. Ehrenberg, G. von Ehrenstein, and A. Hedgran. 1957. Gonad temperatures and spontaneous mutation rate in man. *Nature*, 180: 1433–34.

organisms, wearing by males of trousers instead of kilts or skirts may in fact be the most significant of all inducers of harmful mutations. Let us therefore keep the effects of X-rays and of fallout in proper perspective.

The chemical agents that induce mutation include various kinds of purines and pyrimidines different from those that normally occur in DNA and RNA. Some of the hydrocarbons that also may cause cancer will produce mutations. Caffeine, being a purine, is highly suspect, although it may not be effective. The present evidence is conflicting. In general, however, except for substances such as caffeine which are present in our food or beverages, we are not likely to incur exposure of the reproductive organs to these chemical agents. Here is a problem to be watched without immediate cause for alarm.

Ethical Problems of Selection

Can anything be done to rid the gene pool of its detrimental genes? Can ethical methods be employed to this end?

The most available method would be to use some form of selection, since control of the mutation process itself is at present beyond us. Artificial selection might be applied to prevent the reproduction of carriers of detrimental genes; or measures might be invented to encourage the reproduction and disseminate more widely the good genotypes. Let us look more closely at these negative and positive measures of eugenic selection.

The first difficulty arises because of the recessiveness of most detrimental genes. Harmful dominant detrimental genes are already kept about as low in frequency in the population as is possible. Most bearers of such genes do not reproduce, and most of the harmful dominant genes are new ones just produced by mutation. Our main problem here is the concern which grows from the steadily increasing ability of medical science to lessen or remove the handicap while the harmful gene itself remains intact, to be handed down and consequently to require more medical attention in each succeeding generation. For example, retinoblastoma is a malignant hereditary tumor of the eye which, unattended, is always fatal. Surgery can prevent the spread of the malignancy and often save the vision of the other eye. Being a dominant, the mutant gene that causes retinoblastoma will be expected to be transmitted to half the offspring of any person with the disorder. The question becomes: if we save the lives of these children with retinoblastoma, should they be sterilized to prevent transmission of the gene? Should they be prohibited legally from having children, without sterilization? Should they merely be advised not to have children? Or should nothing be done about the matter? Unfortunately, the latter is only too frequently the solution, even now.

If we adopt severe precautions against the transmission of a dominant gene like that producing retinoblastoma, where do we draw the line with respect to less severe disabilities? Would you sterilize a person with a dominant gene producing a simple visual defect, for example? The criterion seems to devolve upon the social cost of the remedy, glasses being easy and inexpensive to provide, surgery far more costly.

The majority of detrimental genes in the gene pool are, however, recessive. In this case it is necessary, in some way, to detect the bearer before any measures of selection can be taken. Affected individuals with a recessive trait must have carrier parents, of course, but these form a very small proportion of the carriers in the population who did not happen to mate with other carriers. The real hope, in this situation, is to develop technical methods of detecting the carriers, or heterozygotes, by special tests; for, as a rule, it seems they do not possess quite the normal facility for carrying out the chemical step which is blocked, or partially blocked, in the individual with a double dose of the defective gene.

Many ways of detecting the carriers of recessive hereditary disorders are being discovered in the present era of intensive study of human genetics. At a recent Cold Spring Harbor Symposium (1964) no less than three additional genetic disorders were added at one time to the number in which the heterozygote, the "normal" parent, may be distinguished from individuals who do not carry the defective gene at all. It is reasonable to expect that within perhaps two decades genetic clinics for testing prospective brides and bridegrooms will be a regular feature of every first-rate hospital or health department, since by then the number of such detectable defects may reach one hundred or more. Genetic advice to prospective parents can then be based on accurate predictions of the probablity that their offspring may be affected by any one of the hundred or more metabolic errors. When you have located the carriers, however, what measures are to be taken? Is the advice of the heredity counselor sufficient? Are legal measures advisable? There is no unanimity of opinion in these matters, even among geneticists. We must grope our way forward toward a new ethic of reproduction, balancing the good of society against the natural desires of the individual in respect to reproduction. What laws have so far been enacted to deal with this problem are for the most part rash and ill-considered.

Some genes obviously detrimental, like the one that produces Huntington's chorea, may be dominant and yet much delayed in manifestation. The usual age of onset in this disease is between the ages of thirty and forty, but it is often much later. Carriers of the gene marry, raise a family, and sometimes die before the genetic liability is out. Other genes, because of environmental effects or the presence of modifying genes, do not always express themselves. The principal gene predisposing to schizophrenia may be of this kind. Most serious of all is the fact that many socially undesirable traits depend upon multiple genes. General mental inferiority, grading down into imbecility and idiocy, is of this character. In such cases, the negative measures fail.

A further, and still more serious difficulty, lies in the existence of genes which are detrimental in one environment but confer a benefit in another, or of genes in which the heterozygote is more highly favored by selection than either of the homozygous types. A famous example involving both of these situations is that of sickle hemoglobin. Sickle hemoglobin in a double dose, that is, inherited from both parents, produces an almost invariably fatal anemia. In the heterozygote, whom we might designate *SS′*, the single dose of the gene that controls the production of normal hemoglobin prevents the anemia, even though about 40 per cent of the total hemoglobin is of the sickle hemoglobin type, which is low in oxygen-transporting capacity. This condition was first discovered in the United States among Negroes. It is rare among Whites except in the Mediterranean region. It also occurs in some parts of Asia, and in Africa many equatorial Negro tribes possess very high frequencies of *SS′* sicklers, running up to 35 or 40 per cent of all adults. A natural question is why a gene that is so disastrous in the homozygous double dose (*SS*) should ever become common in any population. As a general rule, natural selection keeps the frequencies of lethal genes in a population very low indeed, at a level where the elimination of two lethal genes through death of a homozygote just balances the influx of new mutations of the same sort. And mutation rates are usually very low—scarcely ever above 1 per 40,000.

These considerations led geneticists to suggest that perhaps the sickle hemoglobin gene was preserved in the populations of equatorial Negroes through some advantage of the heterozygote over persons with non-sickling red blood cells. This advantage might have been higher fertility; but an obvious suggestion was provided by the prevalence of certain endemic diseases in those regions where sickle hemoglobin was distributed in the populations. Anthony C. Allison, a young British physician, put the idea to the test. He found 30 volunteers, half of whom were non-sicklers and half sicklers, and all of whom were free of malaria, which Allison suspected as the most likely cause. All 30 persons were injected with blood infected with malaria plasmodium or were bitten by mosquitoes that had fed on infected persons. All 15 of the non-sicklers came down with malaria and were then cured with antimalarial drugs. Of the 15 sicklers, only two persons had an attack of malaria; and their cases were very mild, in contrast to the typical severe malaria of the other group. The evidence from this study has been amply confirmed by other studies and experiments, and it is now quite clear that the presence of sickle hemoglobin in the tribes living in regions of endemic malaria confers great protection. The *SS* homozygotes die of sickle cell anemia, but the *S′S′* homozygotes are very likely to die of malaria during childhood. It is mostly the *SS′* heterozygotes who survive to carry on the tribe. In short, in a population exposed to malaria, which through the ages has been mankind's greatest killer, the "detrimental" *S* gene has proved itself to be of the greatest value in enabling the population to survive.[7]

How many of the variable genes in the human species are of this type, being detrimental under certain conditions and

7. A. C. Allison. 1956. Sickle cells and evolution. *Scient. Amer.*, 195: 87–94.

favorable under others, it is not yet definitely possible to say. Perhaps the rarer mutant types are always detrimental, and are maintained in the gene pool solely by recurrent mutation. On the other hand, the rather abundant polymorphic genes that produce the common differences between individuals of the same race, and between different races, may more likely be of the sort that now and here confer some advantage, but then and there are at a disadvantage. It has recently been demonstrated, for example, that the ABO blood group genes, so long supposed to be neutral in respect to natural selection, are not so at all. Certain of them play a considerable role in preventing the establishment in Rh-negative mothers of sensitivity to the red blood cells of any Rh-positive infants they may bear. The ABO genes are also correlated with the occurrence of certain kinds of organic disease, such as duodenal ulcers and carcinoma of the stomach. And most recently, loss of life in the youngest embryonic stages (early abortion) has been found to be caused by ABO maternal-fetal incompatibility, like that of the rhesus blood group system but occurring much earlier in prenatal life. It has been estimated that as many as 5 per cent of all conceptions die because of this one type of cause. If so, it is a major cause of human death; yet because it occurs so early in life it results in no individual or social problem. The mother often does not even recognize that she has been pregnant.

Beside the genetic problem of detecting the bearers of detrimental genes and the ethical problem of what to do then, we must place the weighty problem of selecting the goals of any program of positive selection upon which we may embark. Clearly, this is no matter for science alone—we are concerned with social values, and which of these is preeminent? In a former essay on this subject I suggested as goals "freedom from gross physical or mental defects, sound health, high intelligence, general adaptability, integrity of character, and nobility of spirit."[8] H. J. Muller selects a somewhat different list: "Genuine warmth of fellow feeling and a cooperative disposition, a depth and breadth of intellectual capacity, moral courage and integrity, an appreciation of nature and of art, and an aptness of expression and of communication;" and on the physical side, "to better the genetic foundations of health, vigor, and longevity; to reduce the need for sleep; to bring the induction of sedation and stimulation under more effective voluntary control; and to develop increasing physical tolerances and aptitudes in general."[9] Now we cannot select for these without having ways and means of defining them precisely and measuring them at least in a roughly quantitative way. Obviously, the psychologist and sociologist will need to do a great deal of preliminary work before genetic analysis and understanding of these traits become possible.

Muller and other advocates of positive genetic selection propose to establish sperm banks in which the sperm of selected donor males might be frozen for use through artificial insemination postponed until a minimum of twenty years after death of the donor. There is no question about the physical feasibility of such measures, and the twenty-year proviso would have the considerable merit of avoiding the possibility of unpleasant personal relationships between donor and recipient, and of a sufficiently long waiting period to permit the real merit of the donor, rather than his temporary

8. Bentley Glass, "Genetics in the Service of Man," in *Science and Liberal Education* (Baton Rouge: Louisiana State University Press, 1959), p. 51.
9. H. J. Muller, "Should We Weaken or Strengthen Our Genetic Heritage?" in H. Hoagland and R. W. Burhoe, eds., *Evolution and Man's Progress* (New York and London: Columbia University Press, 1962), pp. 35, 37.

reputation, to be better revealed. Perhaps, it seems to me, an even longer period than twenty years might be advisable. Many reputations undergo deflation after decease of the person, only to rise markedly after lapse of half a century or more. Also, in my own estimation sperm banks would be of great value in preserving undamaged the reproductive potential of individuals who are particularly liable to severe exposure to high-energy radiations. I would recommend such a measure for consideration on the part of astronauts, for example, since according to our latest information penetration of the Van Allen belts or exposure to radiation from solar flares will expose an individual to very high, if not lethal, doses of protons and neutrons. Persons with occupational hazards in nuclear energy establishments might also find this precaution advisable. There is also evidence that mutations not only accumulate in the germ cells with advancing age but that the older germ cells are more likely to undergo mutation. If that is the case, it may some day become general practice for all male individuals, at least after passing a certain age, to bank their sperms in frozen state, where mutation is at a minimum.

Far more revolutionary developments than the sperm banks will be realized in the next few decades. The culture of pieces of testis or ovary in the laboratory may well lead to the possibility of producing a continuous, inexhaustible supply of the germ cells derived from selected male and female donors, carefully chosen on the basis of the demonstrated high quality of the children produced during their own lifetimes. Fertilization of the human eggs obtained directly from a selected female or from such a laboratory strain can be used to produce embryos that, following a few days of growth in the laboratory and checking to see that all goes well and is normal, can be implanted in the womb of a woman willing to serve as a foster-mother. We might call this procedure "prenatal adoption," since the child would in such a case be the biological offspring of neither the adopting male nor female parent; but the gradual growth of the embryo within the uterus until the end of a regular pregnancy, followed by the usual delivery of the infant, may well be calculated to produce in the foster-mother and father the parental feelings that form so essential a part of parenthood and care of the young. This type of reproductive practice would avoid much of the stigma and legal obstacles that currently beset the practice of artificial insemination, which is held to deprive the male parent of his natural right and legally to be bastardy. Prenatal adoption, according to correspondence I have received, would be welcomed by many couples whose union has been sterile. It will become a practical reality long before the day envisioned by Aldous Huxley, when babies are not only produced by fertilization in the laboratory, but are reared in bottles and doctored by their nutrient media to produce different castes of human beings.

But these visions of a brave new world omit consideration of what I believe to be the major difficulty, namely, the difficulty of really appraising the genotype of the individual who is to serve as donor. Muller himself, with his colleagues, has estimated that the average number of lethal genes, or their equivalent in larger numbers of less detrimental genes, is about four per person. That means an average number of about 10 harmful genes of all grades per person; so very few if any of us are free of harmful recessive genes. How can we select a genotype that on total balance outweighs in good genetic qualities the hidden detrimental genes it contains? How can we prevent inbreeding between the descendants of the same sperm donor, with its likelihood of producing unfortunate persons homozygous for the detrimental genes?

How can we predict the value of a gene in environments other than those in which it is now known to exist? Many such questions appear insoluble at the present time, even though the future may make it possible to answer some of them more definitely. Until that day, I believe, we should proceed with great caution in the endeavor to breed by selection a better race of men. There is even now in the gene pool of mankind as a whole sufficient genetic diversity and potentiality to enable much improvement to be made along more conservative lines. We must spend the next few decades in developing better methods of appraising the nature and merit of individual genotypes.

The Ethical Problems of Gene Flow

Gene flow is the transfer of genes from one population or geographic race to another in which a different percentage of alleles exists. For example, the Mongolian people of central Asia have a high frequency of the blood group gene for group B. Western Europeans have a much lower frequency of this allele and correspondingly higher frequencies of the alternative alleles producing blood groups A and O. Before the Asiatic invasions beginning with Attila in 500 A.D. and continuing at intervals for a thousand years, there was presumably much less B in the European population than there is now. The infusion of the gene for B into the European population was of course accompanied by infusion of all other genes high in frequency among Mongols and lower in frequency among the Europeans. But in the course of time these genes have segregated and recombined so often and with sufficient independence of each other that a present-day European of blood group B is no more likely to possess other characteristically Mongolian genes (the gene for Mongolian eye-fold, for example) than a person who is not of blood group B. The Mongolian genes have become assimilated into the European population, and the process is marked only by the fact that as you leave the Atlantic seaboard of Europe and progress eastward, there is a rather steady increase in the frequency in the population of persons with blood group B.

Gene flow into an insular population like that of Hawaii offers another striking example. If all the immigrants into Hawaii over the past century had remained socially isolated, mating only within their own group, the migrations would have produced no single population, in a genetic sense. The Polynesians who were there first would have remained pure Polynesian, and no gene flow into that population could have been observed. But of course that has not been the case. A very considerable mixture of stocks, Polynesian, Oriental, and European, has occurred.

In the continental United States considerable gene flow has occurred from the White population into the Indian tribal populations and into the Negro population. There are very few Indians remaining without some White ancestry. The analysis of gene frequencies in these tribes bears out this conclusion and enables the geneticist to express the amount of admixture quantitatively. In the case of the Negroes of the United States, and from analyses of the frequencies of about ten different alleles in the African Negroes, the U.S. Negroes, and the Whites, one can conclude with considerable assurance that at the present day most of the Negro population in the United States has a genetic composition about 70 per cent derived from African Negro ancestry and about 30 per cent derived from White ancestry.

In this particular instance, because the period of intermixture, amounting to approximately ten generations, is well-established, one can also study the dynamics of the process of gene flow and make rough predictions on the assumption that the gene flow will continue in the future at the same rate as in the past. The outstanding conclusion from this study is that a very long period of time will elapse before complete assimilation occurs, even if the rate of gene flow, mostly through illegitimate mating until now, is not diminished. Unless it is accelerated, some seventy to eighty generations, or roughly 2,000 years, must pass before we may expect the kind of solution of our racial problems in the mode exemplified by Europe, where nobody thinks about his Mongolian ancestry any more.

The ethical problems of racial relations are illuminated by genetic consideration, but not solved. What we can say is that gene flow does exist, that genetically different populations do become assimilated, that the general trend in the world today is toward a lessening of racial differences and a mingling of human diversity in one larger and larger gene pool. In hybrids between different species of mammals, such as the hybrid between the horse and the ass or the hybrid between the Alaskan brown bear and the polar bear, one often finds hybrid vigor. That is, the hybrid is larger and more vigorous than either parent species, and perhaps, as in the example of the mule, more intelligent. But the interspecific hybrid is also often sterile, as in the case of the mule though not in that of the hybrid bears mentioned. The sterility of interspecific hybrids is itself a barrier that keeps the parent species forever apart and distinct, and from the standpoint of evolution is a good thing, since each species has its own genetic system selected not only for adaptedness to the environment but also selected for internal harmony between the genes—for a coadaptive character, as we say. Hybridization would tend to break down these inner, genetic harmonies, and the failure of the reproductive system to develop properly and to produce functional male and female reproductive cells is one of the first signs of dysharmony. Racists have argued that these facts should be applied also to intermating between the races of mankind. However, there is not the slightest evidence that intermating between the races produces any lessening of fertility whatsoever, and even less that it produces dysharmony in other respects. On the contrary, one might expect some "hybrid vigor" to be displayed, but there is no convincing evidence of that either. Only a single exception to these generalizations may be offered. If a male individual from a human race that was entirely Rh-positive (for example, a Mongolian) were to wed a European Rh-negative female, the probability of having a child with hemolytic disease of the newborn (erythroblastosis fetalis) would be slightly greater than if she married a European, since fewer of the latter are homozygous Rh-positive.

The preliminary conclusions we have reached regarding the advantages of human genetic diversity become strengthened by these considerations. Tolerance for other individuals, of genotypes different from our own, may become easier for us as the manifest differences become personal and individual rather than racial. I do not know. Prejudice and bias will not disappear from human affairs, I am afraid, even long after racial differences have disappeared, some millennia from now. Perhaps what we have to learn from the problems of race, while they are still with us, are the lessons of tolerance and mutual respect, and of fairness in the provision of equal opportunity if there is to be the fullest realization of the capacities inherent in each person's genotype. Surely this is what we mean most deeply by democracy.

3

THE ETHICAL BASIS OF SCIENCE

"And God said, Let there be light."

It has been said that science has no ethical basis, that it is no more than a cold, impersonal way of arriving at the objective truth about natural phenomena. This view I wish to challenge, since it is my belief that by examining critically the nature, origins, and methods of science we may logically arrive at a conclusion that science is ineluctably involved in questions of values, is inescapably committed to standards of right and wrong, and unavoidably moves in the large toward social aims.

In the first of these essays I pointed out that human values have themselves evolved. Man arose after some two billions of years of organic evolution, during which species after species originated, flourished, and fell, or occasionally became the progenitors of species that were new and better adapted, on the basis of the evolutionary scheme of values. Fitness, like it or not, in the long run meant simply the contribution of each trait and its underlying genes to survival. High mortality or sterility led to extinction; good viability and fertility enabled a gene or a trait, an individual or a species to be perpetuated. Man's own values grew out of his evolutionary origins and his struggle against a hostile environment for survival. His loss of certain unnecessary structures, such as bodily hair once clothing was invented; the homeostatic regulation of his body temperature and blood pressure, breathing, and predominant direction of blood flow; his embryonic and fetal growth inside the mother and his prolonged dependence upon maternal lactation; the slow maturation that enabled his brain to enlarge so greatly; the keen vision so necessary to the hunter using his weapons—all of these and many other important human characteristics that contributed to the social nature of man and cemented the bonds of family and tribe arose adventitiously, were improved step by step, and endured because they promoted human survival. Our highest ethical values—the love of the mother for her child and of the man for his mate, the willingness to sacrifice one's own life for the safety of the family or tribe, and the impulse to care for the weak, the suffering, the helpless—all of these too had the same primitive beginnings.

But these ethical values are always, in the evolutionary scheme of things, relative, and never absolute. Whenever the environment becomes changed, the adaptiveness of existing traits becomes maladjusted, and the forces of natural selection lead to a realignment of the genotype, an alteration of the external features and modes of behavior, a modification of the species. What was once good is so no longer. Something else, in terms of reproductive fitness, has become better.

Finally, a crude, embryonic form of science entered the scheme of things, a method of observing and reporting accurately to other persons the movements of the stars, the planets, and the sun and moon, the behavior and migrations of the food animals, the usefulness of certain seeds for food and of certain stems for fibers, the poisonous properties of others. For generations all such practical lore was transmitted only by word of mouth, but the day came when useful knowledge could be written down and preserved inviolate from the forgetfulness and the twists of memory. These were the first simple steps in the development of science: observation, reporting, written records, communication. To such must be added the processes of human reasoning, at first mostly by analogy, so often wrong; then by improved analysis, by deduction from an established truth, or by induction of an established truth from a multitude of observations.

If human progress can be defined at all in objective terms,

it must, as Carl Becker so unforgettably stated in 1935 in his lectures at Stanford University,[1] be defined in terms of the increase of man's power. That power has grown directly out of his science and technology: 450,000 years or more in improving his first crude tools; some 50,000 years in acquiring social organization, agriculture, and community life; about 5,000 years since the invention of written records enormously accelerated progress by enabling each generation to pass on to its descendants the fruits of its own achievements and acquisitions; and finally a mere 350 years of modern science in which the exponential increase of human powers staggers the imagination, and reason itself swoons. This breathtaking view of history is clearly a culmination of the evolutionary process. Man's power over his environment and over himself and his fellows is the result of the extension of the principle of natural selection. In a world of limited space and resources, that which survives is that which promotes survival: durability and powers of multiplication, adaptability and capacity to transmit to others, either by heredity or by teaching. Competing individuals within a population, competing groups within a species, competing species within a community, all must acquire and perpetuate those characteristics that promote their survival, or else become extinct.

There are many ways of promoting survival. One animal may find a niche in the environment where conditions fluctuate little and where food is abundant, and over eons it will undergo no sensible change. Another species, in a highly variable environment and subjected to great interspecific competition, may evolve with astonishing rapidity in a million or even a few hundred thousand years. Survival values are not at all the same for these two species, and who is to say which one

1. Carl Becker. *Progress and Power* (Stanford, Calif.: Stanford University Press, 1935).

is better or more successful in absolute terms? Even more to the point is the fact that characteristics that may promote the survival of an individual may be injurious to the social group or population of which it is a member; or the very same adapted feature that promotes survival of a particular species in a community may be adverse to the welfare of the community as a whole. It is questionable, for example, whether the size and strength, horns or tusks, of great bull males in many mammalian species work for or against the welfare of their own species. By winning in combat the right to reproduce, the male passes on to the next generation the genes that made him so redoubtable. By gathering into a protected harem numbers of females, together with their young, protection of the herd from enemies is enhanced. It seem undeniable, however, that by limiting reproduction in the community to a relatively small number of males the total genetic variability upon which natural selection can play is cut down. In the long run the species may on this account lose its chance to survive. Genetic selection for ever bigger, stronger, more aggressive and more formidably armed males may lead to the evolution of a type so overburdened by the requirements for battle that a shift of environment that is readily tolerated by more variable and less specialized animals spells doom for the battalions of the over-strong. Where are the dinosaurs and titanotheres today?

Large size confers protection from predators, but as bulk increases, more and more massive legs are required to support a terrestrial animal. Mobility is then diminished, and starvation in times of scanty food may be the price that is paid. On the other hand, the tiny shrews lose body heat so rapidly, on account of their small mass, that they must hunt and eat almost constantly, day and night, or quickly starve to death. There is a place for elephants and there is a place for shrews in our present world, but the long-range prospects are poor for both of them. The future looks brighter for species that have achieved some compromise between the respective advantages of large size and small size.

Man's special evolutionary success of course rests on his brain and his ability to learn continuously over a prolonged period of years, so that he can profit from much experience. Should one then conclude that size of brain alone is important? Many mammals have brains of goodly size, but are so fully developed at birth and grow so fast that they mature within one or two years and are old in a decade. In these animals the capacity to learn is severely restricted, not only because their lives are too short to experience a great deal, but also because learning is characteristic chiefly of *young* animals and their days of learning are so quickly past. Flexible, learned behavior is more restricted in mice than in rats, and it is more restricted in rats than in porpoises, whales, or elephants. The human being grows very slowly and lives very long, in comparison with almost all other mammals. Hence his learning may be extended and protracted for many years; all the force of civilization and culture depends upon this condition.

On the other hand, too long a life span for the individual prevents a species from undergoing in freshly altered environments the renewed trials of new mutations, new combinations of genes, and new patterns of social organization. The species in this extremity becomes conservative, and that too may be fatal. The principal characteristic of human culture today is the rapidity with which, under the impetus of science, it is changing. A man of seventy years, unless exceptionally devoted to learning, was educated in a world of fifty years ago, a world of unbelievable cultural antiquity in terms of all we do and prize today. Man has thus worked himself into an evolutionary dilemma of appalling dimensions. He must, to save himself, develop new ways of prolonging education throughout life, of renewing it periodically, and of retaining his mental educability; or else he must curb the impetuous and probably uncontrollable forces of his own scientific and technological enterprise.

Seen aright, therefore, science is more than the instrument of man's increasing power and progress. It is also an instrument, the finest yet developed in the evolution of any species, for the malleable adaptation of man to his environment and the adjustment of his environment to man. If the human species is to remain successful, this instrument must be used more and more to control the nature and the rate of social and technological change, as well as to promote it. It has been well pointed out, by Theodosius Dobzhansky [2] and others, that the rate of biological evolution is appallingly slow in comparison with that of cultural evolution. Man today is probably not, on the average, any more intelligent than his antecedents of Cro-Magnon times, or perhaps even of Neanderthal days, a hundred thousands years ago or more. His genes are much the same. He has merely accumulated the instruments of power and the means of using them, and has learned how to transmit information rapidly and successfully not only to others of his own time but likewise to his descendants. That being so, it must follow that the successful evolution of human culture will depend on the regulation of scientific advance and technological change pari passu with the capacity of the biological man to adjust to change and of his educational methods to bring that adjustment about. Science itself is the potent tool for achieving such regulation. In this sense, at least, science is far more than a new sense

2. Th. Dobzhansky. *Mankind Evolving* (New Haven, Conn.: Yale University Press, 1964), pp. 20, 319.

organ for comprehending the real relations of natural phenomena and the regularities we call "laws of nature." It is also man's means of adjustment to nature, man's instrument for the creation of an ideal environment. Since it is pre-eminently an achievement of social man, its primary function is not simply that of appeasing the individual scientist's curiosity about his environment—on the contrary it is that of adjusting man to man, and of adjusting social groups in their entirety to nature, to both the restrictions and the resources of the human environment.

Ethics is a philosophy of morals, a moral system that defines duty and labels conduct as right or wrong, better or worse. Without becoming embroiled in the problem of the existence of absolute right and wrong in the structure of the universe, the evolutionist is quite prepared to admit the existence of right and wrong in terms of the simple functions of biological structures and processes. The eye is for seeing, an evolutionary adaptation that enables an animal to perceive objects at a distance by means of reflected light rays. Sight conveys information about food, water, danger, companionship, mating, the whereabouts and doings of the young ones, and other vitally important matters. Should one not then say, "To see is right; not to see is wrong." "If therefore the light that is in thee be darkness, how great is that darkness."[3] Similarly, the mind reasons as it does because in the countless ages of evolutionary development its characteristic mental processes led to successful coping with the exigencies of life. Humans whose mental processes, because of different genes, too often led them to wildly erroneous conclusions, did not so often leave children to reason in similar ways. It is thus right to be guided by reason, wrong to distrust it. As the Teacher asked, "Having eyes, see ye not? and having ears, hear ye not?

3. Matthew, chap. 6, v. 23.

and do ye not remember?" [4] Does it not follow, finally, from consideration of the social role and function of science, that it is *right* to utilize science to develop and regulate human social life, adjustment to change, and rate of social transformation? Conversely, it is *wrong*—morally and ethically wrong—not to do so. We must use whatever light and whatever reason we have to chart our course into the unknown.

Those who distrust science as a guide to conduct, whether individual or social, seem to overlook its pragmatic nature, or perhaps they scorn it for that very reason. Rightly understood, science can point out to us only probabilities of varying degrees of certainty. So, of course, do our eyes and ears, and so does our reason. What science can do for us that otherwise we may be too blind or self-willed to recognize is to help us to see that what is right enough for the individual may be wrong for him as a member of a social group, such as a family; that what is right for the family may be wrong for the nation; and that what is right for the nation may be wrong for the great brotherhood of man. Nor should one stop at that point. Man as a species is a member—only one of many members—of a terrestrial community and an even greater totality of life upon earth. Ultimately, what is right for man is what is right for the entire community of life on earth. If he wrecks that community, he destroys his own livelihood. In this sense, coexistence is not only necessary but also right, and science can reveal to us the best ways to harbor our resources and to exploit our opportunities wisely.

THE SUBJECTIVITY OF SCIENCE

From the foregoing description of science as itself an evolutionary product and a human organ produced by natural

4. Mark, chap. 8, v. 18.

selection, it may already be guessed that I do not adhere to the view that either the processes or the concepts of science are strictly objective. They are as objective as man knows how to make them, that is true; but man is a creature of evolution, and science is only his way of looking at nature. As long as science is a *human* activity, carried on by individual men and by groups of men, it must at bottom remain inescapably subjective.

In a penetrating essay entitled "The Mystery of the Sensual Qualities,"[5] Erwin Schrödinger, shortly before his death, dealt with certain of these subjective aspects of science. It is a truism to say that science is based on sense perceptions, the primary observations the scientist makes of his instruments or directly of natural phenomena; but scientific knowledge "fails to reveal the relations of the sense perceptions to the outside world," says Schrödinger. In our picture or model of the outside world, as it is formulated and guided by our scientific discoveries, all sensory qualities are absent. To illustrate this point, which may not be readily admitted by everyone, Schrödinger discusses the relation between the wavelengths of light and the sensation of color. Take yellow, for instance. The wavelengths we sense as yellow are those of about 590 millimicrons, but there is nothing in the frequency to explain the yellowness of yellow. The yellowness is in the mind of the observer, and there seems to be no physical reason why a yellow sensation of color should be experienced when wavelengths of 590 mμ enter the eye rather than a red or blue or any other sensation. In fact, in a color-blind man the sensation evoked by wavelengths of 590 mμ is something quite different. A totally color-blind scientist may do refined experiments with instruments that measure wavelengths

5. E. Schrödinger. *Mind and Matter* (Cambridge: Cambridge University Press, 1958), pp. 88–104.

of light, refract them, focus them, do all sorts of things with them. But the totally color-blind scientist can never conceive what anyone else means by "yellow," and indeed we have no real assurance that anyone else experiences what we ourselves do when we see yellow. All we know, in daily life and in science, is that persons whom we agree are competent observers agree to call some sensation "yellow" which they experience when stimulated by light of 590 mμ.

Schrödinger pointed out, too, that radiation in the neighborhood of wavelengths of 590 mμ is not the only stimulus that will evoke the sensation of yellow. One can take waves of 760 mμ, which alone are pure "red," and mix them in a certain proportion with wavelengths of 535 mμ, by themselves "green," and the "competent observer" simply cannot distinguish the mixture from the color of pure 590 mμ waves. "Two adjacent fields illuminated, one by the mixture, the other by the single spectral light, look exactly alike, you cannot tell which is which." Moreover, states Schrödinger, this effect cannot be foretold from the wavelengths. There is no numerical connection between the physical wavelengths and the mixture. The mixture that makes yellow has been determined empirically. There is no general rule that a mixture of two spectral lines of light matches one lying between them. Thus, a mixture of "red" and "blue" wavelengths from the ends of the spectrum produces "purple" color, but there is no single spectral wavelength that evokes purple at all.

The same truth holds for each and every other kind of primary sensation, whether it be taste or odor, sound vibrations, or touch. A simple prick with a pin on the skin evokes different sensations—warmth, cold, pain, pressure—depending upon the site of the prick and the connections to the central nervous system of the particular receptors which have been stimulated. It is a well-known law of physiology that the nature of the sensation is not primarily a matter of the nature of the stimulus, but of the receptor. Either a receptor does not respond at all, or it responds by evoking the same particular sensation in every instance. Mild pressure on the eye makes one *see* colors; a severe blow makes one *see* stars. The eye can only see, and within it the individual receptors respond only to light, irrespective of wavelength if they are rods, or to light of specific wavelengths if they are cones.

To extend Schrödinger's analysis, we may well recognize that our sensory apparatus and the structure of our nervous systems, within which arise our sensations, grow and develop as they do from the first beginnings in the human embryo because of the particular genetic constitutions we inherit from our parents. First and foremost, we are *human* scientists, not insect scientists, nor even monkey scientists. The long past of our evolutionary history, with its countless selections and rejections of various kinds of genes and combinations of genes, has made us what we are. Try as we will, we cannot break the bounds of our subjective interpretations of the physical events of nature. We are born blind to many realities, and at best can apprehend them only by translating them by means of our instruments into something we can sense with our eyes or ears, into something we can then begin to reason about by developing abstract mental concepts about them, by making predictions on the basis of our hypotheses, and by testing our theories to see whether reality conforms to our notions.

Within recent years many psychological experiments have shown beyond any doubt that even the simplest concepts developed in the mind on the basis of sensory experiences are profoundly and inescapably subjective. They are related to past experience and to the capacity to learn from experience.

A very young kitten learns from its experiences how to interpret visual cues of distance and direction in space, and shows alarm when placed on a "visual cliff." [6] Yet it must learn this. It must first build into its mental structure some idea of how simple space relations are related to visual cues. Only thereafter can it function effectively in the real world it lives in. But a kitten, birdling, or human infant deprived of the opportunities to learn such things, and to learn them at the appropriate age, may be forever afterwards crippled in its mental constructs just as literally as an animal that has lost a limb is forever mutilated.

This line of reasoning leads us to the conclusion that the objectivity of science depends wholly upon the ability of different observers to agree about their data and their processes of thought. About quantitative measurements and deductive reasoning there is usually little dispute. Qualitative experiences like color, or inductive and theoretical types of reasoning, leave great room for disagreement. Usually they can be reduced to scientific treatment only if the subjective color can by agreement be translated into some quantitative measurement such as a wavelength, only if the reasoning can be rendered quantitative by use of a calculus of probability. It nevertheless remains a basic fact of human existence that the subjectivity of the individual personality cannot be escaped. We differ in our genes, each of us possessing a genotype unique throughout all past and future human history (unless we happen to possess an identical twin). To the extent that our genes endow us with similar, though not identical, sensory capacities and nervous systems, we may make similar scientific observations, and we may agree to ignore the existence of the variables in our natures that prevent us from

6. Eleanor J. Gibson and R. D. Walk. 1960. The "Visual Cliff." *Scient. Amer.*, 202: cover and 64–71.

ever making exactly the same measurements as someone else or arriving at exactly the same conclusions. But it is perilous to forget our genetic individuality and our own uniqueness of experience. These form the basis of the ineradicable subjectivity of science. In the last analysis science is the common fund of agreement between individual interpretations of nature. What science has done is to refine and extend the methods of attaining agreement. It has not banished the place of the individual observer, experimenter, or theoretician, whose work is perhaps subjective quite as much as objective.

These considerations may seem so obvious as not to require the emphasis just given them. Yet I believe not. Somehow there has crept into our writings about the nature and methods of science a dictum that science is objective while the humanistic studies are subjective, that science stands outside the nature of man. What a profound mistake! Science is ultimately as subjective as all other human knowledge, since it resides in the mind and the senses of the unique individual person. It is constrained by the present evolutionary state of man, by the limitations of his senses and the even more significant limitations of his powers of reason. All that can be claimed for science is that it focuses upon those primary observations about which human observers (most of them) can agree, and that it emphasizes those methods of reasoning which, from empirical results or the successful fulfillment of predictions, most often lead to mental constructs and conceptual schemes that satisfy all the requirements of the known phenomena. Just here, in general, lies the superior service of mathematics to science. Its logic is less disputable than others, although some persons may deny that merit to statistical methods of dealing with probabilities. (Perhaps one of the greatest services to be expected of computers is that they can test and validate statistical theory.)

SCIENCE, INTEGRITY, AND INTELLECTUAL FREEDOM

From a consideration that science is a human activity, inescapably subjective, and a product of biological evolution, it is possible to derive a genuine ethical basis of science. J. Bronowski, in an essay entitled "The Sense of Human Dignity," [7] has sketched a treatment that serves well for a beginning. The values and duties which are the concern of ethics are social, he affirms. The duties of men hold a society together, he says; and "the problem of values arises only when men try to fit together their need to be social animals with their need to be free men." Philosophy must deal with both the social and individual aspects of value. Most philosophical systems have found this very difficult to do. Thus dialectical materialism swings far to the side of social values and leaves little scope for individual freedom. Positivism and analytic philosophy, as typified by Bertrand Russell and Wittgenstein, on the other hand, emphasize the values of the individual.

Hence, continues Bronowski, because the unit of the positivist or the analyst is one individual man, "positivists and analysts alike believe that the words *is* and *ought* belong to different worlds, so that sentences constructed with *is* usually have a verifiable meaning, but sentences constructed with *ought* never have." [8]

The issue, then, is simply whether verification can indeed

7. J. Bronowski. *Science and Human Values* (New York: Julian Messner, 1956), pp. 63–94.
8. *Ibid.*, p. 72.

be assumed to be carried out by one man. Bronowski concludes, and I find it impossible to deny, that in the practice of science this supposition is sheer nonsense. Verification depends completely on the existence of records that may be consulted, of instruments that may be used, of concepts that must be understood and be properly utilized. In all these ways, knowledge is a social construct, science a collective human enterprise; and verification is no procedure of the naked, unlettered, resourceless man but an application of the collective tools of the trade and the practiced logic of science to the matter at hand. It is a fallacy to assume that one can test what is true and what is false unaided. But then it must follow that all verification, all science, depends upon communication with others and reliance upon others. Thus we come straight to the *ought* of science, for we must be able to trust the word of others. A full and true report is the hallmark of the scientist, a report as accurate and faithful as he can make it in every detail. The process of verification depends upon the ability of another scientist, of any other scientist who wishes to, to repeat a procedure and to confirm an observation.

Neither the philosophy of dialectical materialism nor that of the individualist accords with the basic nature of man and of scientific truth. The extreme social position leaves no room for the conscience of man and the exercise of intellectual freedom because the community dictates what is right and what a man *ought* to do. Yet the positivist's position is also faulty because "how a man *ought* to behave is a social question, which always involves several people; and if he accepts no evidence and no judgment except his own, he has no tools with which to frame an answer." [9] Again, "All this

9. *Ibid.*, p. 72.

knowledge, all our knowledge, has been built up communally; there would be no astrophysics, there would be no history, there would not even be language, if man were a solitary animal."[10]

"What follows?" asks Bronowski, and answers: "It follows that we must be able to rely on other people; we must be able to trust their word. That is, it follows that there is a principle which binds society together, because without it the individual would be helpless to tell the true from the false. This principle is truthfulness. If we accept truth as a criterion, then we have also to make it the cement to hold society together."[11] Whence he derives the social axiom:

> *"We OUGHT to act in such a way that what IS true can be verified to be so."*

So Bronowski. If his reasoning be accepted, and to me it seems unarguable, we must conclude that the cement of society is nothing less than the basic ethical tenet of science itself. The very possibility of verification—the assurance that one's own conclusions are not dreams, hallucinations, or delusions—rests upon confirmation by others, by "competent" observers whom we trust to tell the truth.

The Scientist's Integrity

Ethics rests upon moral integrity. Science rests upon the scientist's integrity. This is so implicit in all of our science that it is rarely expressed and may be overlooked by novice or layman. Bronowski mentions examples of what happens when this basic moral commandment is violated by a scientist. Lysenko is held up to scorn throughout the world and

10. *Ibid.*, p. 73.
11. *Ibid.*, pp. 73–74.

eventually is deposed.[12] Kammerer commits suicide.[13] It is very interesting that both of these notorious examples, and others less well known, such as that of Tower, a quondam professor of biology at the University of Chicago, have related to attempts to "prove" or bolster the theory of the inheritance of acquired characteristics. The singular attractiveness of this theory for violators of scientific integrity is no doubt owing to its social significance, since if true it would offer a quick and easy way for man to control the direction of human evolution and would lessen the obdurate qualities of genes modifiable only by mutation in uncontrollable directions.

It is not so generally recognized by these superficial evolutionary philosophers that, if true, the inheritance of characters produced by means of modifications of the environment would call in question the value of all evolutionary gains, since the modified characters would themselves have no real genetic permanence and would shift and vary with every change of environment. They also do not recognize one of the most essential aspects of heredity, the protection of the genetic nature against vicissitudes. The reason why death is so necessary a part of life, as I have pointed out in the first of these essays, is that the ground must be cleared for fresh life. The reason why the genotype must remain unmodifiable by ordinary environmental causes is because the course of life for every individual involves the cumulative effects of injury, disease, and senescence. The new generation must indeed start *fresh,* that is, free from all the disabilities incurred during life by its parents and remoter ancestors. Evolution

12. Bentley Glass. 1948. Dialectical materialism and scientific research. *Quart. Rev. Biol.,* 23: 333–35; D. S. Greenberg. 1965. Lysenko, Soviet science writes Finis to geneticist's domination of nation's biological research. *Science,* 147: 716–17.

13. R. Goldschmidt. 1949. Research and politics. *Science,* 109: 219–27.

through the action of natural selection upon mutations, most of which are harmful and non-adaptive while only a rare exemplar among them is possibly advantageous, is a process slow in the extreme. But it preserves the gains of the past, and it permits every generation to be born anew, unburdened by decrepitude, to try out its varieties of genotypes in each niche of the environment.

The loss of scientific integrity through deliberate charlatanry or deception is less common than the violation of scholarly honesty through plagiarism. The theft of another man's ideas and the claim that another's discovery is one's own may do no injury to the body of scientific knowledge, if the substance of what is stolen be true. It may even do no harm to the original discoverer, who may be dead or in no need of further credit to advance his own career. It is nevertheless a canker in the spirit of the thief and does damage to the fabric of science by rendering less trustworthy the witness of the scientist.

Plagiarism shades into unacknowledged borrowing. Which of us in fact can render exactly the sources of all his ideas? Psychologists have now amply demonstrated the ease with which self-deception enters into the forgetfulness of borrowed benefits. The wintry wind of man's ingratitude blows only on the donor of benefits forgot. Around the self-deluded recipient blow only the mildest, gentlest zephyrs of spring. The newer patterns of scientific publication and support of research have multiplied a thousandfold the opportunities for the scientist's self-deception. Editors of scientific journals today customarily rely upon referees for opinions regarding the merit of manuscripts submitted for publication. The enormous expansion of scientific activity and the development of hundreds of new specialities have made this referee system necessary. The best referee is of course some other scientist who is working closely on the same scientific problems but is not associated with the author in the actual work—in other words, a competitor, since we must not forget that scientists are people who must earn a living, and since compensation and repute follow productivity and publication. Natural selection is at work among scientists, too! What is most alarming about the workings of the referee system is not the occasional overt lapse of honesty on the part of some referee who suppresses prompt publication of a rival's work while he harvests the fruit by quickly repeating it—perhaps even extending it—and rushing into publication with his own account. What is far more dangerous, I believe, because it is far more insidious and widespread, is the inevitable subconscious germination in the mind of any referee of the ideas he has obtained from the unpublished work of another person. If we are frank with ourselves, none of us can really state whence most of the seminal ideas that lead us to a particular theory or line of investigation have been derived. Darwin frankly acknowledged the ideas of Malthus which led him to the Theory of Natural Selection; but although he was one of the most honest of men, and one who was deeply troubled when Alfred Russel Wallace sent him in 1858 the brief paper setting forth his own parallel derivation of Darwin's theory, Darwin nevertheless never made the slightest acknowledgment of the idea of natural selection which he had surely read in the work of Edward Blyth in 1835 and 1837.[14] We may guess that Darwin's reasoning at the time went rather as follows:

> Blyth's conception is that natural selection leads to a restriction of hereditary variation in

14. Loren C. Eiseley. 1959. Charles Darwin, Edward Blyth, and the Theory of Natural Selection. *Proc. Amer. Phil. Soc.*, 103: 94–158.

> populations. Through elimination of the more variable specimens in a species, nature keeps the species true to type and prevents it from becoming maladapted to its environment. Blyth's Natural Selection is not an evolutionary force at all, but instead is a force for maintenance of the status quo.

Yet it is very hard to understand why, when the full significance of the action of natural selection dawned upon Darwin, he did not re-examine the ideas of Edward Blyth. It should have been perfectly evident to him that the very same force that would eliminate variation and maintain the status quo of the species in a stationary environment would operate quite differently in a changing environment. Will we then ever know the extent to which Darwin was really indebted to Blyth, or how the ideas he probably rejected as invalid actually prepared the way for his reception of Malthus' thoughts in 1838?

The conscientious referee of unpublished scientific manuscripts is similarly a gleaner in the harvest fields of others. The only possible way to avoid taking an unfair advantage would be to refuse to referee any manuscripts that might conceivably have a relationship to one's own research work. The consequences for editors left with piles of unevaluated manuscripts might become desperate, were there not, as I believe, a reasonable solution in the possibility that the role of referee could be limited to scientists who have ceased to do active experimental work themselves. What with the increasing life span and the large number of retired but mentally vigorous older scientists, the supply of competent referees would perhaps be sufficient. To be sure, the criticism may be raised that the older scientific men cannot properly evaluate the significance and merit of really revolutionary new ideas and lines of work. Neither, for the most part, can the young! A combination of older referees in the field and younger ones knowledgeable but not working in the same specialty might solve this difficulty.

What has been said about referees applies with even greater force to the scientists who sit on panels that judge the merit of research proposals made to government agencies or to foundations. The amount of confidential information directly applicable to a man's own line of work acquired in this way in the course of several years staggers the imagination. The most conscientious man in the world cannot forget all this, although he too easily forgets when and where a particular idea came to him. This information consists not only of reports of what has been done in the recent past but of what is still unpublished. It includes also the plans and protocols of work still to be performed, the truly germinal ideas that may occupy a scientist for years to come. After serving for some years on such panels I have reached the conclusion that this form of exposure is most unwise. One simply cannot any longer distinguish between what one properly knows, on the basis of published scientific information, and what one has gleaned from privileged documents. The end of this road is self-deception on the one hand, or conscious deception on the other, since in time scientists who must make research proposals learn that it is better not to reveal what they really intend to do, or to set down in plain language their choicest formulations of experimental planning, but instead write up as the program of their future work what they have in fact already performed. Again, the integrity of science is seriously compromised.

Science and Intellectual Freedom

The first commandment in the ethical basis of science is complete truthfulness, and the second is like unto it:

Thou shalt neither covet thy neighbor's ideas nor steal his experiments.

The third is somewhat different. It requires fearlessness in the defense of intellectual freedom, for science cannot prosper where there is constraint upon daring thinking, where society dictates what experiments may be conducted, or where the statement of one's conclusions may lead to loss of livelihood, imprisonment, or even death.

This is a hard ethic to live by. It brought Giordano Bruno to the stake in 1600. The recantation of Galileo was an easier way; the timidity of Descartes and Leibniz, who left unpublished their more daring scientific thoughts, was understandably human but even less in the interest of science or, ultimately, of the society that felt itself threatened. Whether in the conflict of science with religion, or with political doctrine (as in Nazi Germany), or with social dogma (as in the Marxist countries), scientists must be willing to withstand attack and vilification, ostracism and punishment, or science will wither away and society itself, in the end, be the loser.

From the beginning the inveterate foe of scientific inquiry has been authority—the authority of tradition, of religion, or of the state—since science can accept no dogma within the sphere of its investigations. No doors must be barred to its inquiries, except by reason of its own limitations. It is the essence of the scientific mind not only to be curious but likewise to be skeptical and critical—to maintain suspended judgment until the facts are in, to be willing always, in the light of fresh knowledge, to change one's conclusions. Not even the "laws" of science are irrevocable decrees. They are mere summaries of observed phenomena, ever subject to revision. These laws and concepts remain testable and challengeable. Science is thus wholly dependent upon freedom—freedom of inquiry and freedom of opinion.

But what is the value of science to man, that it should merit freedom? There are those, indeed, who say that science has value only in serving our material wants. To quote one of them: "Science is a social phenomenon, and like every other social phenomenon is limited by the injury or benefit it confers on the community. . . . The idea of free and unfettered science . . . is absurd." Those were the words of Adolf Hitler, as reported by Hermann Rauschning.[15] In Soviet states a similar view is held officially; and in the Western democracies, likewise, not a few scientists as well as laymen have upheld a similar opinion. The British biologist John R. Baker has pointed out that this view shades through others, such as the admission that scientists work best if they enjoy their work, and the supposition that science has value in broadening the outlook and purging the mind of pettiness, to the view that a positive and primary value of science lies in its creative aspect "as an end in itself, like music, art, and literature." [16] "Science aims at knowledge, not utility," says Albert Szent-Györgyi [17]; and Alexander von Humboldt wrote in his masterpiece, *Cosmos*, that "other interests, besides the material wants of life, occupy the minds of men." [18]

It is readily demonstrated that the social usefulness of the conclusions of science can rarely be predicted when the work is planned or even after the basic discoveries have been made.

15. H. Rauschning. *Hitler Speaks: A Series of Political Conversations with Adolf Hitler on His Real Aims* (London: Butterworth, 1939), pp. 220–21.

16. John R. Baker. *Science and the Planned State* (New York: Macmillan, 1945).

17. A. Szent-Györgyi. 1943. Science needs freedom. *World Digest*, 55: 50.

18. A. von Humboldt. *Cosmos: A Sketch of a Physical Description of the Universe*, tr. E. C. Otté (London: Henry G. Bohn, 1849).

John R. Baker, in his book *Science and the Planned State,* has cited numerous examples that show the impracticability of a too narrowly planned program of scientific research. The sphere of investigation must be determined by the investigator's choice rather than by compulsion—by perception of a problem to be solved rather than by a dogma to be accepted blindly. Science must be free to question and investigate any matter within the scope of its methods and to hold and state whatever conclusions are reached on the basis of the evidence—or it will perish. But science is represented only by the individual scientists. These persons must acknowledge the moral imperative to defend the freedom of science at any cost to themselves. Every Darwin needs a Thomas Henry Huxley. Every Lysenko demands his martyred Vavilov, his hundreds of displaced geneticists before he is finally deposed. Modern science, from its very beginnings near the end of the sixteenth century, became immediately concerned with a major political issue, the freedom of the scientist to pursue the truth wherever it might lead him, even though that conclusion might be highly disturbing to settled religious beliefs or social conventions and practice. The pyre of Bruno and the ordeal of Galileo led directly in spirit to the attacks on Charles Darwin 250 years later and to latter-day instances of the social suppression of scientific findings. The distortion of genetics by racists in Nazi Germany finds a counterpart in the United States; Mendelian genetics in the U.S.S.R., and the nutritive qualities of oleomargarine in Wisconsin share a similar fate. The third commandment then reads:

> Thou shalt defend the freedom of scientific investigation and the freedom of publication of scientific opinion with thy life, if need be.

Science and Communication

Inasmuch as science is intrinsically a social activity and not a solitary pleasure, another primary aspect of the ethics of science is the communication to the world at large, and to other scientists in particular, of what one observes and what one concludes. Both the international scope of scientific activity and the cumulative nature of scientific knowledge lay upon the individual scientist an overwhelming debt to his colleagues and his forerunners. The least he can do in return, unless an ingrate, is freely to make his own contributions a part of the swelling flood of scientific information available to all the world.

There are at least five distinct obligations his indebtedness places upon each scientist. The first of these is the obligation to publish his methods and his results so clearly and in such detail that another may confirm and extend his work. The pettiness and jealousy that lead some scientists, in their effort to stay ahead of the ruck, to withhold some significant step of procedure or some result essential to full understanding of the stated conclusions have no place in the realm of science. In other instances it is sheer laziness or procrastination that is at fault. Whatever the only too human reason, science suffers.

A second obligation that is far more frequently neglected is the obligation to see that one's contributions are properly abstracted and indexed, and thus made readily available to workers everywhere. Many scientists ignore this obligation completely. Yet, as the sheer volume of scientific publication passes a half-million and soon a million articles a year, it is obviously insufficient to add one's own leaflet to the mountains of paper cramming the scientific libraries of the world. The need to have scientific findings abstracted and indexed has been fully recognized by such international bodies as the

International Council of Scientific Unions; its Abstracting Board has urged every author to prepare an abstract in concise, informative style, to be printed at the head of each scientific paper; and the editors of most scientific journals have now made this a requirement for acceptance and publication of a paper. Nevertheless, few authors prepare their abstracts without a reminder, and few heed the requirements for a concise, informative summary that will permit proper indexing of the major items treated in the paper.

A third obligation is that of writing critical reviews, which will be true syntheses of the knowledge accumulating in some field. I firmly believe that there is no scientific activity today more necessary and at the same time less frequently well done than this one. I have said elsewhere:

> To be sure, the scientist seeks for facts—or better, he starts with observations. . . . But I would say that the real scientist, if not the scholar in general, is no quarryman, but is precisely and exactly a builder—a builder of facts and observations into conceptual schemes and intellectual models that attempt to present the realities of nature. It is the defect and very imperfection of the scientist that so often he fails to build a coherent and beautiful structure of his work. . . .
>
> This insight, this vision of the whole of nature, or at least some larger part of it, exists in all degrees among the individuals we call scientists. The man who adds his bits of fact to the total of knowledge has a useful and necessary function. But who would deny that a role by far the greater is played by the original thinker and critic who discerns the broader outlines of the plan, who synthesizes from existing knowledge through detection of the false and illumination of the true relationships of things a theory, a conceptual model, or a hypothesis capable of test?
>
> The creativity of scientific writing lies precisely here. The task of the writer of a critical review and synthesis that fulfils these objectives and meets these criteria is not only indispensable to scientific advance—it surely constitutes the es-

sence of the scientific endeavor to be no mere quarryman but in some measure a creator of truth and understanding. The aesthetic element that makes scientist akin to poet and artist is expressed primarily in this broader activity.

The critical nature of the critical review grows from our constant forgetfulness of all this. The young scientist is taught carefully and methodically to be a quarryman or a bricklayer. He learns to use his tools well but not to enlarge his perspective, develop his critical powers, or enhance his skill in communication. The older scientist is too often overwhelmed by detail, or forced by the competition of the professional game to stick to the processes of "original research" and "training." The vastness of the scientific literature makes the search for general comprehension and perception of new relationships and possibilities every day more arduous. The editor of the critical review journal finds every year a growing reluctance on the part of the best qualified scientists to devote the necessary time and energy to this task. Often it falls by default to the journeyman of modest talent, a compiler rather than critic and creator, who enriches the scientific literature with a fresh molehill in which later compilers may burrow.[19]

All this need not be so, but it will remain so without a deeper sense of the obligation of the scientist to synthesize and present his broadest understanding of his own field of knowledge. Tomorrow's science stands on the shoulders of those who have done so, no less than on the shoulders of the great discoverers. Thanks be to those in our time—a considerable number—who merit this accolade!

A fourth obligation is communication to the general public of the great new revelations of science, the important advances, the noble syntheses of scientific knowledge. There have always been a few eminent scientists who did not scorn to do this. Thomas Henry Huxley, John Tyndall, and Louis

19. Bentley Glass. 1964. The critical state of the critical review article. *Quart. Rev. Biol.*, 39: 182–85.

Pasteur set the pattern in the nineteenth century, and in our own time there have indeed been many who followed their precedent. Yet there seems to be a growing tendency to turn this obligation over to professional science writers who, however good, should not replace the direct, personal, and authoritative appeal of the scientist to the general public. As our culture and civilization become day by day more completely based on scientific discovery and technological application, as human exploration becomes ever more restricted to the endless frontiers of science, every citizen must know whereby he lives and whereupon he leans. A democracy rests secure only upon a basis of enlightened citizens who have imbibed the spirit of science and who comprehend its nature as well as its fruits. In fulfilling the requirement of our age for the public understanding of science the scientist must shirk no duty.

A final obligation in the total purview of scientific communication is the obligation to transmit the best and fullest of our scientific knowledge to each succeeding generation. It is well said that genetic transmission of human characteristics and powers is now far overshadowed by cultural inheritance. The transmission of knowledge is the role of the teacher, and the obligation of the scientist to teach is his last and highest obligation to the society that gives him opportunity to achieve his goals.

To every scientist—to some sooner, to some only late—there comes the realization that one lifetime is too short and that other hands and other minds must carry on and complete the work. Only a few scientists are therefore content to limit their entire energies to exploration and discovery. Research is one end, but the other must be the training of the new generation of scientists, the transmission of knowledge and skill, of insight and wisdom. The latter task is no less necessary, no less worthy. From the beginnings of human history, the exponentially accelerating growth of human power . . . has required each generation to instruct and inform the next.

This is the challenge that faces every teacher of a science as he steps into the classroom or guides the early efforts of an individual student. Here, in this sea of fresh faces—here, amidst the stumblings and fumblings—may be the Newton or Einstein, the Mendel or Darwin of tomorrow. For few—so very few—men are self-taught. The teacher cannot supply the potentialities of his students, but he is needed to see that the potentialities will unfold, and unfold fully. His is not only the task of passing on the great tradition of the past, with its skills and accumulated knowledge; he must also provide breadth and perspective, self-criticism and judgment, in order that a well-balanced scientist may grow to full stature and continue the search.

Of all the resources of a nation, its greatest are its boys and girls, its young men and women. Like other material resources, these can be squandered or dissipated. They are potential greatness, but they are only potentialities. Science creates knowledge and knowledge generates power, but knowledge resides only in the minds of men who first must learn and be taught, and power is tyranny unless it be guided by insight and wisdom, justice and mercy. The greatest of men have been teachers, and the teacher is greatest among men.[20]

THE SOCIAL AND ETHICAL RESPONSIBILITIES OF SCIENTISTS

The scientist escapes lightly—instead of ten commandments only four: to cherish complete truthfulness; to avoid self-aggrandizement at the expense of one's fellow-scientist; fearlessly to defend the freedom of scientific inquiry and opinion; and fully to communicate one's findings through primary publication, synthesis, and instruction. Out of these

20. Bentley Glass. 1964. The scientist and the science teacher. *AAUP Bull.*, 50: 267–68.

grow the social and ethical responsibilities of scientists that in the past twenty years have begun to loom ever larger in our ken.

These may be considered under the three heads of proclamation of benefits, warning of risks, and discussion of quandaries. The first of these, the advertisement of the benefits of science, seems to be sufficiently promoted in these days when science is so well supported by government and private agencies and when grants are justified on the basis of social benefits. Every bit of pure research is heralded as a step in the conquest of nuclear or thermonuclear power, space exploration, elimination of cancer and heart disease, or similar dramatic accomplishments. The ethical problem here is merely that of keeping a check-rein on the imagination and of maintaining truthfulness. But the truth itself is so staggering that it is quite enough to bemuse the public. Who, at the beginning of this century, or even fifty years ago, would have regarded as practical possibilities such dreams as the control of nuclear energy, desalination of water, radar, transistors, masers and lasers, cheap and effective means of birth control, hybrid corn, antibiotics and wonder drugs, the elimination of tuberculosis and malaria, pesticides and biological ways of eliminating or controlling pests, and a hundred other discoveries any one of which would have revolutionized our ways of life? Science, the cornucopia of material bounty, has in fact changed human history, altered national economics, and transformed man's conception of the universe and his place in it.

Since 1945 more and more scientists have become engaged in warning of the great risks to the very future of man of certain scientific developments. First the atomic bomb and then the hydrogen bomb brought swift realization of the possibility of the destruction of all civilization and even the extinction of all human life were a nuclear war to break out. The atomic scientists, conscience-stricken, united to secure civilian control of nuclear energy. Albert Einstein and Bertrand Russell issued an appeal to scientists to warn the world of the tragic consequences of overoptimism and of an unbridled arms race. Joined by a dozen notable scientists, they initiated the "Pugwash" Conferences on Science and World Affairs in 1957. In these conferences scientists of East and West sat down together to talk, in objective scientific terms, of the military and political problems of the world and their resolution. It was not that the scientists at all felt themselves to be more highly qualified than diplomats and statesmen, economists or lawyers, to find solutions of the most difficult and delicate problems of international relations. They acted on two grounds only: that they understood the desperate nature of the situation about which the world must be warned in time; and that they hoped discussions by persons accustomed to argue in objective, scientific terms might pave the way for better understanding and more fruitful negotiation on the part of officials. In the ensuing discussions of the effects of fallout from nuclear weapons tests on persons now living and on the generations yet unborn, scientists played a very important role. In no small measure, I believe, historians of the future will recognize how great a part was played by the scientists in bringing about the partial weapons test ban. Scientists are now deeply involved in politics, and naturally enough often on both sides of the argument, for although they may agree upon the basic scientific facts which are relevant to the issue, there are rarely enough established facts to clinch the argument and there is always room for differences of opinion in interpreting the facts. In these matters the ethic of the matter requires the scientist to state his opinion on matters of social concern, but at the same time to

THE HUNT LIBRARY
CARNEGIE INSTITUTE OF TECHNOLOGY

distinguish clearly between what he states to be fact and what opinion he holds. Moreover, his opinion about matters within his technical sphere of competence is an "informed" opinion; his opinion about other matters, even other scientific matters, is that of a layman. He must in all honesty make clear to the public in what capacity he speaks.

Nuclear war is only one of the dire misfortunes that are poised above the head of modern man. The unrestricted and appalling rate of population increase in most countries of the world, if projected just a few decades into the future, staggers the imagination with its consequences. Effective control of the birth rate is the only conceivable answer to effective reduction by modern health measures of the death rate. This is the world problem second in importance at the present time, and must engage the conscience of the scientist. As the physicist struggles to confine nuclear energy to peaceful pursuits, the biologist enters the struggle to control man's sexual desires and to reduce the threat they pose to the well-being of populations everywhere.

The problem of the future is the ethical problem of the control of man over his own biological evolution. The powers of evolution now rest in his hands. The geneticist can define the means and prognosticate the future with some accuracy. Yet here we enter the third great arena of ethical discussion, passing beyond the benefits of science and the certain risks to the nebulous realm of quandaries. These were outlined in some detail in the second of these essays. Man must choose goals, and a choice of goals involves us in weighing values—even whole systems of values. The scientist cannot make the choice of goals for his people, and neither can he measure and weigh values with accuracy and objectivity. There is nonetheless an important duty he must perform, because he and he alone may see clearly enough the nature of the alternative choices, including laissez faire, which is no less a choice than any other. It is the social duty and function of the scientist in this arena of discussion to inform and to demand of the people, and of their leaders too, a discussion and consideration of all those impending problems that grow out of scientific discovery and the amplification of human power. Science is no longer—can never be again—the ivory tower of the recluse, the refuge of the asocial man. Science has found its social basis and has eagerly grasped for social support, and it has thereby acquired social responsibilities and a realization of its own fundamental ethical principles. The scientist is a man, through his science doing good and evil to other men, and receiving from them blame and praise, recrimination and money. Science is not only to know, it is to do, and in the doing it has found its soul.

Date Due